A Unified Health Service

ABOUT THE AUTHORS

David Owen, M.A., M.B., B.Ch., is Member of Parliament for Plymouth (Sutton) and a Member of the Board of Governors of Charing Cross Hospital. Before entering Parliament he was neurological and psychiatric registrar to St. Thomas' Hospital, London.

Nigel Weaver, Dip.Soc. Studies, is a hospital administrator at a London teaching hospital.

Bernie Spain, M.A., Dip.Psych., is a research worker in social and community studies in London.

A Unified
Health Service

Editor: DR. DAVID OWEN, M.P.

Authors:

DAVID OWEN, BERNIE SPAIN, NIGEL WEAVER

1966
THE QUEEN'S AWARD
TO INDUSTRY 1966

PERGAMON PRESS

OXFORD · LONDON · EDINBURGH · NEW YORK
TORONTO · SYDNEY · PARIS · BRAUNSCHWEIG

PERGAMON PRESS LTD.,
Headington Hill Hall, Oxford
4 & 5 Fitzroy Square, London W.1
PERGAMON PRESS (Scotland) LTD.,
2 & 3 Teviot Place, Edinburgh 1
PERGAMON PRESS INC.,
44–01 21st Street, Long Island City, New York 11101
PERGAMON OF CANADA LTD.,
207 Queen's Quay West, Toronto 1
PERGAMON PRESS (AUST.) PTY. LTD.,
19a Boundary Street, Rushcutters Bay, N.S.W. 2011, Australia
PERGAMON PRESS S.A.R.L.,
24 rue des Écoles, Paris 5^e
VIEWEG & SOHN GMBH,
Burgplatz 1, Braunschweig

Printed in Great Britain by A. Wheaton & Co., Exeter

08 103886 0 (flexicover)
08 203886 4 (hard cover)

Contents

Introduction

On 6 November 1967 Mr. Kenneth Robinson, Minister of Health, made a statement concerning the administrative structure of the medical and related services which made it quite clear that the Government were considering as a matter of some urgency legislation to achieve greater integration of the Service.

The Minister said* :

> I have begun full and careful examination of the administrative struc-
> ture that is needed not only for today, but looking ten or twenty years
> ahead. I am aware that some people say that the tripartite structure is
> unwieldy and that to have three types of separate authority is not the
> right way to achieve that degree of integration which a proper service
> to the individual requires. However, the nature of any changes that ought
> to be made requires a most careful examination and this is what I have
> now begun. I should make it clear that my studies will relate entirely to
> the administrative pattern. I am not considering the possibility of what
> would amount to an alternative health service, as is sometimes sug-
> gested, involving for instance, a switch in financing from the public
> to the private sector.
>
> There are good reasons why these studies should proceed now in
> parallel with, and of course without prejudice to the enquiries on related
> matters already being pursued. A Royal Commission is studying the
> whole area of local government in England, and the Seebohm Committee
> is considering the local authority and allied personal services in England
> and Wales. I have told these bodies of my aim, which is to have proposals
> about the administration of medical and related services ready to be
> looked at alongside their own recommendations. I have also informed the
> Royal Commission on Medical Education of my intention, and shall be
> keeping in touch with my Right Hon. friend the Secretary of State for
> Wales in connection with the forthcoming reorganisation of local govern-
> ment in Wales which may be relevant.

Since the Minister talks of producing only a Green Paper, that is a discussion paper, it is obvious that no firm conclusions can

* *Hansard*, Monday, 6 November 1967, Vol. 753, No. 5, Medical and Related Services (Administrative Structure), col. 643.

be reached on the basis of his publication, and that much debate must occur before any definite proposals are framed. We have, therefore, decided to publish our recommendations, which are the outcome of our own discussions over the past year, at this time, and without waiting to hear what are the Minister's conclusions. His proposals will be framed as a result of departmental recommendations, and it seems that there is a real danger that the civil servants will advise the creation of *ad hoc* health authorities. We believe that this would be a great mistake, and put forward the suggestion in this book that a structure should be found for the health services which will link health administration to both local and central government.

We realize that our solution is a compromise and will be criticized particularly by those who believe that integration should be achieved by the direct transfer of the hospital and general practitioner services to local government. The solution we advocate, however, does involve having the same physical boundaries for health at regional and local level as for local government. Elected councillors would also serve as of right on the regional and area health boards. In this respect none of our arguments for integration into both tiers of the local government system would be invalidated if it were decided to integrate under the overall control of local government.

CHAPTER 1

The Evolution of the National Health Service

THE quality of the National Health Service is the concern of every citizen in the country, for there can be no one who is unaware of the possibility that, at some time, frequently or infrequently, they will have cause to call upon its services.

Because we live in a time of rising standards and aspirations, the demands on the Service inevitably increase, and the pace at which the N.H.S. can move to meet these demands will always be a matter for legitimate argument. Yet the growth of the N.H.S. is obviously limited by the same physical parameters as those which operate on all the other essential services, whether it be, for example, the police, the fire brigade, or the armed forces. All are deemed vital to the welfare and survival of the community but all make claims on our financial and manpower resources which, if allowed to proceed unchecked, would enforce an imbalance that would mitigate against the overall good of the community. It is quite clear that somewhere a balance has to be struck and the growth of these services set against the competing demands of all other claims on our national resources.

Unfortunately rational choice in these particular fields is bedevilled by their emotional content. Most people tend to adopt a position in which their own particular fears and prejudices dominate the priority which they ascribe to a particular service. At the extreme end of the scale the pacifist objects in principle to the armed forces, and the Christian Scientist to the N.H.S., but in-between the vast majority of the population only determine their priorities when forced by circumstance to use the particular service. However, by their very nature these services have an unpredictable demand that imposes the necessity for a high state of readiness and an increasing sophistication in equipment and skills.

This conflict of priorities is, of course, inherent in any human activity, and it is in order to resolve these difficulties and to be able to choose that we have evolved a political system. It seems therefore quite inevitable that the politician will be involved in the decision making and strategy to be adopted for any of the services on which the community depend. It is reasonable to expect that such services will be treated by politicians responsibly, and to claim that they should be removed from the area of political choice is unrealistic and even naïve.

The N.H.S., because it enters into the privacy and intimacy of an individual's life, is peculiarly vulnerable to bitter criticism although it also receives immense gratitude. It is wholly desirable and healthy that the public, as both client and consumer, should feel involved in the N.H.S., and it would be foolish for politicians or those employed by the N.H.S. to resent public examination of the Service. As shown by various surveys, it is certainly true that at present the public are reasonably content with the overall service that they are given. The N.H.S. will never be able to meet all the demands that society imposes on it, but it should be able to claim that all reasonable requests are satisfied and that it provides overall an organization that is sensitive and sympathetic to the needs of its users.

Dissatisfaction, it can be reasonably argued, will always exist within any health service. One major reason which makes this likely is that the great bulk of medical care is confined to repairing and assisting an ageing or defective bodily system. We all want, when ill, to not only be cured but revived and renewed, yet it is a sad fact of life that the dramatic cure represents a small fraction of the work of any health service. In consequence, disillusionment with the inevitable limitations of treatment is expressed quite understandably against the one structure that is cast in the role of the provider of good health.

It is necessary to state these limitations at the outset, not out of a sense of defeatism or despair, but because it is all too easy to judge the N.H.S. in isolation and to insist that because it is concerned with life and death its demands must override all others. It is sometimes claimed that the N.H.S. should be outside politics, run by an independent body financed and staffed without any regard to other requirements, and able to grow at a rate which would keep pace with the most recent advances in treatment. Often the most extravagant statements come from seemingly the most responsible sources. The amazing improvements that have occurred over the last two decades are forgotten in the frustration induced by almost any limitation. We hear interminably about shortages, whether of equipment, nurses, technicians, or doctors and of old-fashioned buildings, equipment, and practices. Exaggerated claims are made for health services that exist in other countries, and alternatives to the N.H.S. are assiduously canvassed by proponents of private medical practice.

The American system quite clearly shows that private insurance cannot, except at a crippling expense, cover a family for all medical contingencies, and very few people have advocated an all-embracing system such as this for Britain. Most schemes presented for reform involve either subsidizing private medical care, or reducing the Exchequer subsidy to public medical care, but neither of these suggestions involve any fundamental structural change to the existing system. What is incredible is that, given a fairly widespread dissatisfaction within the Service, and particularly amongst doctors, with the present working of the system, how little serious attention has been given since its inception to radical reform of the structure of the present Service while maintaining the existing financial arrangements.

It is frequently argued that the only real problem with the N.H.S. is a shortage of money, though the manpower situation is increasingly causing concern. These are genuine and important issues, and rightly they give rise to anxiety amongst not only the persistent critics of the N.H.S. but also its most fervent admirers. But there is another factor which has been much neglected and that is the efficient use of the existing resources. If only some of the energy and talent expended on criticizing those deficiencies that are reputed to arise from providing care *free* at the point of consumption had been directed at ensuring that the care was provided *efficiently* at the point of consumption, there would now exist a far better N.H.S. It is to the provision of a more efficient service, even accepting for the moment the present limits of finance and manpower, that this book is aimed. We believe that the quality of the Service can be improved while retaining the essential principle of universal free care on which the N.H.S. was founded.

One tends to see the establishment of the N.H.S. solely in terms of one Minister, Aneurin Bevan, and the socialist convictions of the 1945 Labour Government. In fact, like most major pieces of legislation, the N.H.S. Act of 1946 [1] evolved from a number of differing government proposals and was influenced by powerful pressure groups throughout its formative stages. [2] The first outline of a N.H.S. from a government came when Ernest Brown, then Minister of Health in the wartime coalition in 1941, announced the decision to form a national hospital service after the war and to start a survey of the existing services. During the war the Emergency Medical Service began to bring the voluntary and local government hospitals together and to create a climate for co-operation. The 1942 Beveridge Report [3] also gave emphasis to the initial government declaration by stressing that a comprehensive social security system could not operate without a National Health Service.

In March 1943 Ernest Brown presented proposals which comprised a unified system with a central government department, advised by a central council, and based on a system of large local government areas formed either by joint authorities or with a regional structure. The opposition to this plan was immense, particularly from the medical profession, who thought it owed too much to proposals put out by the National Association of Local

Government Officers and the Society of Medical Officers of Health.

In February 1944 the new Minister of Health, Henry Willink, produced a White Paper[4] which modified some of the unpublished earlier proposals but retained the idea that the local organization of all the services should be vested in joint authorities, being advised, however, by an appointed council. General practitioners would be under contract to a central medical board, though this was later changed to a local committee based on the National Health Insurance system. It is worth noting that, by 1945, Willink had achieved a substantial measure of agreement for his proposals and even local government preferred the Willink proposals to the 1946 Act. This is not surprising, for though he advocated regional councils, these were to be responsible mainly for hospital and specialist services in an advisory capacity. Local government was still to retain executive powers and the voluntary hospitals their separate identity. The Willink proposals, as they emerged, increasingly abandoned a unified administrative structure and neatly balanced all the conflicting pressures so that the original Brown idea of a unified service was gradually discarded.

In view of these proposals it is in some ways not surprising that "The National Health Service Bill–Summary of the Proposed New Service", that was presented to Parliament in March 1946 dropped the proposals for a unified structure. Its only major new proposal was that ownership of the hospitals and the organization of consultant services of all kinds should be transferred to a Regional Hospital Board. It therefore laid down the basic tripartite structure that exists today, with the establishment of the local authority health services separate from the general medical services administered through executive councils.

Aneurin Bevan later admitted that it was not unnaturally a compromise solution. Yet even with the benefit of hindsight it is difficult to see how anyone at that time could have imposed a unified structure. The medical profession did, and would have, fought bitterly against any proposal to establish the local authorities as their employer, and it was a hard enough battle even to abolish the independence of the voluntary hospitals. It is also worth noting that then, as now, a fundamental review involving local government was in prospect, but it was believed that this would not recommend the large areas that, for hospital administration, were felt to be a necessity. Hence the proposal for a regional structure for the hospital service that would cover a large number of local authorities. Even in 1956 the Guillebaud Report[5] felt that the administrative structure should remain unaltered. But they reached this conclusion after an extensive examination of one possible alternative, namely "one which would integrate the three branches of the National Health Service without depriving the local authorities of their existing domiciliary health functions". This would have meant transferring the hospitals and general medical services to the local authorities. A recurrent argument against any change was that it was still a young service having been in existence only 7 years when the report was written and that it needed a period of stability to plan ahead. It is interesting, however, to note the memorandum by Sir John Maude: "Reservations about the structure of the National Health Service", pointing out the weaknesses which seemed to be inherent in the administrative structure of the Service, whereby the Service is operated by three sets of bodies having no organic connection with each other and financed by three methods, one of which differs radically from the other two. He summarized the disadvantages which can be traced to the tripartite division as:

    (a) the administrative divorce of curative from preventive medicine and of general medical practice from hospital practice and the overlaps, gaps and confusion caused thereby.

    (b) the predominant position of the hospital service and consequent danger of general practice and preventive and social medicine falling into the background.

On balance at that time, he concluded that to transfer to local authorities the hospital and specialist services was inopportune, but concluded that at some future date, accompanied by adequate reorganization of local government administration and finance, such a change might be expedient.

It was not until 1962, with the publication of the Porritt Report[6] advocating Area Health Boards (A.H.B.s), that the critics of the tripartite system had any authoritative backing for a unified structure. The Porritt Report was, however, rather vague in its detailed examination of what this concept of the area health board actually entailed. This was not surprising for the report was prepared by doctors for their own profession with no outside member and no representative from local government. It is, however, of major importance in that the recommendation for A.H.B.s has been largely accepted by the medical profession so that in principle, at least, there is a willingness to work towards a unified administrative structure. It is also significant in that doctors, the most conservative element in any change in the existing pattern, have expressed their dissatisfaction with the present structure and need for a new framework better suited to the development of an integrated community-orientated health service.

It is interesting to trace the reasons for this change in attitude. Ever since the inception of the N.H.S. the Ministry of Health has advocated, mainly by ministerial circulars, the need for co-ordinating the different elements of the Service and has actively sought to encourage co-operation. Recently the Ministry has sought to integrate the tripartite organization by reasserting the importance of the health centre as a place from which hospital consultants, local authority clinical staff, and family doctors can all work, and where the climate for a community approach can flourish.

Between 1948 and 1964 only twenty-one new health centres were built, but by March 1976 local authorities forecast that they will have provided 300 health centres. The question which the Ministry has so far evaded is whether this form of integration is sufficient. With the publication of reports on the maternity, mental health, and family doctor services, it becomes increasingly clear that even given the will to co-ordinate the Service, the existing administrative framework actively impedes integration and that, in a service where shortages of manpower are endemic, there is clear-cut evidence of overmanning and overlapping as a direct result of the administrative pattern. What gives cause for more concern is the persistent evidence that because of the system's inherent inefficiencies, patients themselves suffer, falling victims to the divided responsibility and isolation that all too frequently reduces the concept of community care to an illusion. It would be extraordinary for any major industry, whether manufacturing or service, to retain unchanged its administrative structure for over 20 years. Yet this is exactly the situation which has existed within the N.H.S. The forthcoming reorganization of local government that is heralded in the proposals for Wales[7] and will inevitably arise from the royal commissions studying England and Scotland,[8] should serve as the stimulus to adopt a completely new framework for the administration of the N.H.S. It is the aim of this book to try to clothe the proposals for A.H.B.s with some substance, and to indicate the main principles on which any such reconstruction should be based.

CHAPTER 2

The Present Structure of the National Health Service

THE first section of the National Health Service Act, 1946, which came into force on 5 July 1948, lays down that it shall be the duty of the Minister of Health to "promote the establishment in England and Wales of a comprehensive health service designed to secure improvement in the physical and mental health of the people of England and Wales" and that the Service be available to all citizens.

The Service is divided into three parts:

(a) Hospital and Specialist Services.
(b) Local Health Authority Services.
(c) Executive Council Services.

The scope of each sector, and the number of authorities concerned, are shown in Fig. 1.

The Hospital and Specialist Services

Under the Act the first attempt was made to provide one national service in place of the former multitude of unrelated and independent voluntary hospitals and those provided by the local authorities. Certain private nursing homes or hospitals run by religious orders, private companies, or others (like Free-masons), were disclaimed under the provisions of the Act.

The national service is financed centrally from the Exchequer, via the Ministry of Health, but delegated responsibility for the provision of services is given to the Minister's agents—Regional

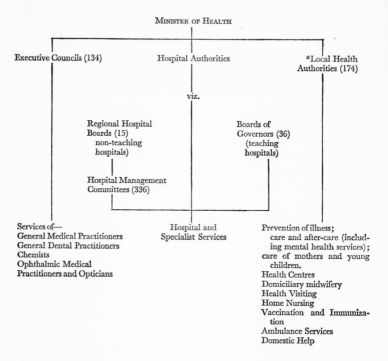

FIG. 1. DIAGRAM OF THE STRUCTURE OF THE NATIONAL HEALTH
SERVICE.

Hospital Boards, Boards of Governors, and Hospital Management Committees.

For administrative purposes there are two kinds of hospital—teaching and non-teaching, and the former designation shows that these hospitals, in association with a university, provide the additional function of facilities for training undergraduate or postgraduate medical students. Teaching hospitals are administered by boards of governors, and amongst them rank such famous hospitals as St. Bartholomew's, St. Thomas's, and Guy's, whilst in the provinces the former voluntary infirmaries are joined into groups such as the United Leeds Hospitals, or United Cambridge Hospitals. Postgraduate teaching hospitals are concentrated on London, and work in co-ordination with institutes for teaching purposes—hence National Heart Hospital and the Institute of Cardiology for the postgraduate study of heart diseases. There are altogether thirty-six teaching hospitals—twenty-six of them in London.

Non-teaching hospitals are grouped in local districts, each group under the aegis of a Hospital Management Committee (H.M.C.) and each group is theoretically able to offer within it a balanced range of normal specialties. The exception is that hospitals dealing with mental illness or mental sub-normality still tend to be independent groups, although this practice is now in decline. There are 336 H.M.C.s, although the number is reduced annually as administrative amalgamations take place.

H.M.C.s as will be seen from the diagram, are linked with central control by fifteen regional hospital boards. These boards were set up in 1948 without very exact reference to existing local authority boundaries, in areas large enough to plan regional hospital services effectively. The difficulty over liaison with local boundaries is illustrated by the opening sentence of the description of the area served by the North West Metropolitan Regional Hospital Board:

> The administrative counties of Bedford, Hertford (except the parts included in the East Anglian Region [i.e. urban district of Royston] and North East Metropolitan Region [i.e. Hertford, Bishop's Stortford, Cheshunt, Hoddesdon, Sawbridgeworth and Ware, and three rural districts]) and Middlesex (except the part included in the North East Metropolitan Region) [i.e. Edmonton, Tottenham and Enfield].

The catchment area continues with similar treatment for Berkshire, Buckinghamshire, and London County Council.

It is the responsibility of these regional hospital boards to undertake with the Minister, and in collaboration with the boards of governors, the planning, provision and supervision of a co-ordinated hospital and specialist service for its region, including the control of capital works and the appointment of senior medical staff. The Regional Board also appoints the chairman and members of H.M.C.s.

The H.M.C.s are responsible to the regional board for the day-to-day administration of the hospitals in their group. In this connection they are given the responsibility of controlling revenue expenditure (covering maintenance of hospital premises, purchase of stores and equipment, employment and dismissal of staff) and other details that arise in the course of hospital administration.

The Ministry see these bodies as "agents" acting on the Minister's behalf, and central policy is made known through a series of Hospital Memoranda, as well as letters on individual topics which are addressed to the secretary of the appropriate authorities. This agency relationship is reflected in the tone of circulars; "This Memorandum *commends* to hospital authorities a report . . . . The Minister accepts the report in principle and *asks* Boards and Committees to give full co-operation in implementing its recommendations" (our italics). In point of fact the Ministry or Exchequer auditors usually satisfy themselves that the Minister's earnest entreaties are observed.

The size of these bodies vary. H.M.C.s generally number from 15 to 20 people, boards of governors 20–25, and regional boards 25–30. There is some common membership between all three.

It is important to note that in England and Wales boards of governors of teaching hospitals exempted from the regional hospital board framework, enjoy direct rights of access to Ministry officials, and an independence in the provision of services. Initially in London, at least, they served no defined area of population in respect of hospital services, selecting their patients instead from nation-wide referrals. In the past few years this has changed, as the wider improvement of medical services has made it less essential to send patients to these central hospitals, and undergraduate teaching hospitals have begun to take on "district" responsibilities for all who live in certain defined postal districts. The proposed designation of a University Hospital is contained in the Health Services and Public Health Bill. [1]

Administratively each one of these three bodies has certain officers—the secretary to the board or H.M.C. and a treasurer. At group level the secretary is the co-ordinator of all the hospitals within the group, as well as the committee's chief officer. At regional level there is also a senior administrative medical officer (with appropriate supporting staff) and his title describes his particular sphere. There is rarely an equivalent at hospital or H.M.C. level, although in mental hospitals some medical superintendents still remain as the officer responsible for medical matters. Normally an advisory medical committee, through its chairman, fills this role.

The national pattern of hospital spending is shown in Tables 1 and 2.

Local Health Authority Services

Local health authorities are county or county borough councils, who have functions under Part III of the National Health Service Act.

Interestingly enough, one of the first clauses in Part III says: "it shall be the duty of every local health authority to provide, equip, and maintain . . . . 'health centres' " at which facilities for any or all of the following services are to be made available:

> General medical services
> General dental services
> Pharmaceutical services
> Specialist and other services for out-patients
> Any other local health authority services
> Health education

For various reasons it has only been in the past 2 years that there has been any rapid movement towards the provision of

TABLE 1. PATTERN OF HEALTH SERVICE FINANCE

	Percentage of gross national product
The N.H.S., 1966	4·6
Education, 1966	5·7
Housing, 1966	2·8
Defence, 1966	6·8

Over half the N.H.S. cost is for hospitals—£800 million per year. Teaching hospitals take about 14% of total revenue expenditure and about 20% of capital expenditure, although they only constitute 6½% of the bed allocation.

TABLE 2. PATTERN OF HOSPITAL REVENUE EXPENDITURE

	Percentage of total expenditure	
Salaries and wages: Medical staff (including doctors paid by regional hospital board)	10·3	
Nursing staff	26·9	
Building and engineering	2·4	
Administrative and clerical	3·5	
Other staff	22·1	
	65·2	65·2
Provisions		7·6
Staff uniforms and patients clothing		0·9
Drugs		2·6
Dressings		0·7
Medical and surgical appliances and equipment		4·1
General services (power, light, etc.)		6·5
Maintenance of buildings, plant and grounds		3·7
Domestic repairs, renewals, and replacements		1·5
Central administration		2·4
Other hospital expenditure		4·8
		100·0

(SOURCE: *Summarized Accounts of Hospital Authorities for the Financial Year 1964–65.*)

health centres. The new role and importance of such centres today is discussed in a subsequent chapter.

Prior to the 1946 Act, local authorities had permissive powers for services in connection with the care of mothers and young children, but section 22 placed the express duty on authorities to make arrangements for the care of expectant and nursing mothers and young children. These services are usually operated from welfare clinics, and include the provision of ante- and post-natal clinics, day nurseries, infant welfare, and welfare foods. Linked closely with this is the provision of a domiciliary midwifery service. At present the local authority nurses may have the mothers they were looking after transferred to hospital for confinement and delivery, and are precluded from attending them in hospital or nursing homes. Under the 1967 Health Service and Public Health Bill, provision is made for health visitors and nurses to attend patients elsewhere than in their homes, thus theoretically, allowing for more interchange. After the birth of all children it is mandatory on local authorities that families must be seen, at least once, by a health visitor. Health visitors are concerned with the health of a family as a whole, and their role as health educators or family social workers has been the subject of much discussion in latter years. The shortage of health visitors is particularly acute—5500 were employed in 1965, while the local authority health and welfare plans anticipate 8942 required by 1976. Home nurses (8100 in 1965) attend to those requiring nursing in their own homes, and district nurses are becoming increasingly involved in the care of those with chronic illnesses. Home helps are available in all local health authority areas, and each year provide practical assistance to over 420,000 people, for chronic or mental illnesses, maternity or other social reasons. One clause in the Health Service and Public Health Bill will make this service mandatory and also empower local authorities to make available laundry facilities as part of the service.

The ambulance service is provided under section 27 of the Act and is to be used for the "conveyance of persons suffering from illness or mental defectiveness or expectant mothers from places in their area to places in or outside their area". Over 21 million people are carried annually.

Care of the mentally disordered is included within the compass of the services mentioned already, but, in addition, local authorities have a duty to provide services specifically directed to the prevention of mental illness and the care and aftercare of those suffering from mental disorder. Since the Mental Health Act, 1959, which was the result of the report of the Royal Commission on Mental Health, 1954–7, there has been an increasing emphasis on community, rather than hospital care, and it has fallen on local authorities to provide this. The range of community services is wide: social workers; training centres for the subnormal who cannot be taught at school; training centres for work, occupation, and social training of subnormals; occupation centres for those with mental illness; residential accommodation —either by boarding out or in hostels. At the end of 1965 a total of 161,763 people were receiving such local services.

Other residential accommodation is provided under Part III of the National Assistance Act, 1948, and provides for the provision of homes for the elderly or those temporarily homeless. Just over 100,000 mainly elderly people were accommodated in such residential homes in 1965. The provision of temporary residential accommodation has been the subject, during 1966–7, of much national debate, and in 1965 nearly 12,500 were in such accommodation.

The elderly also receive other services from the local health authority—the most important ones being the provision of meals and recreational amenities. In both these services voluntary organizations, either under subvention from or in close collaboration with local authorities often provide the personnel and sometimes premises. Other welfare services available include chiropody; welfare of blind, deaf and handicapped; social work; occupational therapy; adaptation of houses to lessen handicaps; sickroom and other equipment and assistance with individual holidays. There are a miscellany of other health and welfare functions provided under various Acts. In brief these are:

(a) Prevention of illness and after-care (N.H.S. Act, 1946).
(b) Prevention of the spread of infectious diseases (Public Health Acts, 1936 and 1961).
(c) Vaccination of smallpox contacts.
(d) Health education (P.H. Act, 1936, and N.H.S. Act, 1946).
(e) Registration and inspection of private nursing homes (P.H. Act, 1936, and Nursing Homes Act, 1963).
(f) Registration of charities for disabled persons (National Assistance Act, 1948).
(g) Registration of homes for disabled, elderly, and mentally ill (National Assistance Act, 1948).
(h) Port Health (shipping and airports) (Public Health Regulations, 1966).
(i) Imported food (Food and Drugs Act, 1955).
(j) Hygiene, unfit food, meat inspection, and slaughterhouse inspection (Food and Drugs Act, 1955).

The administration of the health functions is laid down in the National Health Service Act which stipulates that every authority shall establish a Health Committee, to refer to that committee all matters relating to the discharge of their functions under the Act and except in the case of urgent matters the local health authority should consider a report by the committee before exercising their functions.

The administrative structure varies, but most large counties have found it desirable to split the county into areas, each with a sub-committee and local direction. The senior officer is the medical officer of health, with departmental heads (chief welfare officer, superintendent midwife, chief public health inspector) as appropriate. Financing is partly from local rates, but also extensively through grants in aid by central government departments.

The Seebohm Committee was set up to consider local authority social work. In Scotland the Kilbranden Report on the same topic paved the way for a White Paper *Social Work and the*

Community[2] which envisages the establishment, *inter alia*, of a new social work department, headed by a director of social work. This department would incorporate the existing welfare and mental health, domestic help sections, as well as the probation and child care services, not at present administered by the local authority health committees. These ideas are incorporated in the Social Work (Scotland) Bill presented to Parliament in March 1968.

Executive Councils

The administrative body responsible to the Minister for the general medical, dental, pharmaceutical, and supplementary ophthalmic services is the local executive council. In general there is an executive council for each county or county borough area, although some executive councils cover more than one area.

The function of the executive councils is to administer the general practitioner services (payment of fees, distribution of practices equitably, maintenance of obstetric lists, and registration of patients) and to enter into contracts with general practitioners, dentists, pharmacists, and opticians for these professions to render their services to members of the public seeking them.

The executive council hears complaints (other than those involving wholly professional matters) arising from the services it administers and advises the Minister where a complaint is held to be justified.

The senior official is the clerk to the executive council, who is a layman. The council is composed of twenty-four members nominated by the professions concerned, the Minister, and the local health authority. It is required by law to appoint a finance committee, and medical, dental, and pharmaceutical committees. The supplementary ophthalmic services committee is also mandatory to make arrangements for sight-testing and the supply of optical appliances. The council is financed entirely from Exchequer funds.

Conclusion

This brief, and necessarily factual chapter is designed to show the existing framework of the N.H.S. The administrative arrangements within the Ministry of Health have not been examined, as it is not relevant to the consideration of this book.

CHAPTER 3

The General Practitioner at Present

THE new disciplines and techniques which have been applied in the field of social medicine have demonstrated both the deficiencies and the possible improvements in the structure of a health service that is still firmly entrenched in the nineteenth century. Nowhere is this more evident than in general practice. No reform of the health service can hope to succeed unless it carries with it the 20,000 general practitioners who provide the essential and most sensitive primary link between the individual and the national health services. But "The industrial revolution has passed general practice by; it remains a cottage industry, under organized, under capitalized, and overworked." [1]

We must therefore re-examine the present role and functions of the G.P. and consider how best to reinstate the front-line doctor as a specialist in primary diagnosis and domiciliary care, which is his right and proper function in any effective health service. The deficiencies in the present G.P. service which we pin-point cannot be attributed to individual negligence so much as to the system in which he is forced to work. It is our contention that only by cardinal reforms can we really help the G.P. to achieve the higher standard of medical care which he, himself, wishes to provide. The G.P. himself must realize that a refusal to change his position will only result in furthering the divisive structure of the N.H.S. and impeding progress towards higher standards. Many features of general practice as it is at present conceived in this country do not work satisfactorily to the benefit of the consumer or the doctor. At the same time there are other aspects of the N.H.S. which are just as unsatisfactory and also in urgent need of reform. The answer to the G.P.'s problems lie ultimately in radical administrative changes which would allow the evolution of a more cohesive and efficient service. The W.H.O. Expert Committee on general practice which reported in 1964, after asserting the vital importance of general practice, went on:

> This is not to say that all is well in general practice today or that it should be left to continue as it now is . . . . general practice suffers from defects that must be remedied in order to bring medical care up to the standards now required by medical progress and often demanded by the public.

Study is only just beginning on ways of measuring the quality of medical care, whether inside or outside the hospital. The problem is to determine how many people are ill, whether their illnesses might have been prevented, and how good their treatment has been. These things are notoriously difficult to measure. The numbers of deaths from specified groups of the population provides one method of measurement, although, of course, mortality rates provide a measure for only a small part of illness in an era of successful control of many previously fatal diseases.

The picture that one obtains of G.P. efficiency from mortality studies is fair but not flattering. A useful index, with relevance to general practice, is perinatal mortality, that is still births and deaths in the first week of life. During one week of 1958 there was a national study of all the births which occurred in Britain (perinatal mortality survey). [2] A great deal of information was collected about these births, about the prenatal care that had been given, and about the deaths which occurred in the subsequent 3 months. This allowed comparisons between the standards of hospital and G.P. care.

A recent study in the Oxford Region [3] of obstetric practice among G.P.s confirms that there are still grave deficiencies. In the absence of hospital facilities for all deliveries, it seems reasonable to argue that "high-risk" mothers should have priority for hospital beds, since G.P.s have neither the facilities nor the experience to deal effectively with serious obstetric complications.

To define the "high-risk" group accurately requires ease of referral of pregnancies to a consultant obstetrician. This study showed, however, that half G.P. maternity units had no formal arrangements for ante-natal consultations with specialists, and only 5 per cent were integrated with consultant units. This is all the more alarming since the study shows that 20 per cent of G.P. units did not have facilities to give anaesthetics safely, and 34 per cent had no equipment for the resuscitation of the newborn. Since half of all units studied were sited 10 miles or more from the nearest centre with a consultant obstetrician, this means that in many cases, babies requiring resuscitation would have to travel by ambulance several miles to the nearest centre where adequate treatment was available. Some would probably die on the way and many receive damage to the central nervous system due to the delay in treatment.

Turning to other studies of how G.P.s work and the quality of the equipment that they use, again the picture is far from rosy. This is not something that is recent or the result of the N.H.S. In 1950 a New Zealand G.P., Joseph Collings, published in the *Lancet* a survey of British general practice which revealed widespread deficiences. [4] This caused quite an uproar at the time, and stimulated further studies, notably by a staff member of the B.M.A., [5] and one by Lord Taylor [6]. Although the later studies were aimed to stress the good features of British general practice, their authors had to admit that all was not well with the British G.P. and his ways of working. In the Taylor study, a quarter of the observed doctors were deemed to be unsatisfactory despite the fact that the doctors studied had been selected on the basis of their colleagues' esteem. These studies were carried out some time ago, but subsequent research, whether on the ways G.P.s use drugs or diagnostic services such as X-rays or pathological tests, or the ways they call on domiciliary nursing services, reveal wide variations between practices, variations that do not fit at all well with the patterns of illness and disability. [7]

It is often claimed that the G.P. plays a vital part in the

organization of the health services because he is in a unique front-line position. He is the first person to whom the sick person turns, and it is his decision that determines whether the patient is referred to hospital or is recommended for some other form of care. As such, the G.P. is often portrayed as the leader in a domiciliary team of specialists and ancillaries. How well does he, in fact, fit this dynamic role? Relations between the G.P., nurses, and social workers are far from satisfactory. Until very recently collaboration between doctor and public health nurses was almost non-existent. It is now improving, partly as a result of the policy of attaching these nurses, particularly health visitors, to general practices rather than having the nurse work from the public health department. However, such schemes at present affect only about 15 per cent of health visitors and there are still strong antipathies between many doctors and these nurses. Relationships with home nurses are usually said to be excellent, but when the extent of communication is analysed, it transpires that in towns, nurses work for several doctors and do not always seem to discuss patients regularly each week, let alone each day. Indeed, a standard method of communication is still by notes left in the patient's home. There is ample evidence that social workers could give valuable assistance with many of the problems presented to the G.P. One study showed that a considerable number of patients needed the help of a skilled caseworker. [8] In practice, social workers, such as child care officers, often complain that communications between themselves and the G.P.s is defective. Sometimes this is simply because doctors are busy, but in addition doctors do not seem to understand the work and the skills of social workers. Indeed, why should they? Doctors are taught little about social casework or the social services. Professional social work is changing rapidly and without constant information about these developments, G.P.s cannot be expected to understand modern practice. How, then, can the G.P. collaborate effectively, let alone lead?

If we examine the G.P.'s relationships with hospitals and hospital specialists, again the picture is not encouraging. In the recent official report on general practice, the Gillie Report, reference was made to home visits by specialists. [9] The number of these domiciliary consultations is rising in the N.H.S., but it is estimated that "consultation with both doctors present at the patient's home takes place today at less than half of the visits, and this proportion is probably falling". Furthermore, a study of out-patients who attended Guy's Hospital showed that in 40 per cent of cases it was the patient, not the G.P., who chose his hospital. [10] This suggests that the G.P. is not selecting for his patients the particular consultant by whom he will be treated. A study of G.P.s' letters to hospitals also reveals inadequacies, for instance the reasons for consultation and the social background of the patient are often insufficiently described. [11] Some hospital doctors complain that patients have not even been examined before referral. When the patient actually arrives at the hospital there are big differences in what happens to patients from different practices. For some practices many patients are usually admitted directly for treatment, but from others the patients are frequently transferred to other departments, suggesting incorrect initial referral. [12] Consequently the hospital rather than the G.P. plays the major role in selecting the correct service and controlling the patient's treatment.

The image of the G.P. as the personal doctor providing continuity of care throughout the patient's life is also one which is not always supported by the facts. One important function of the G.P. in this role is to ensure that the patient he has referred to hospital receives adequate care and is satisfied with his treatment —to act as a kind of hospital ombudsman. Few G.P.s in fact manage to see their patients while in hospital, and they are all too frequently made to feel unwelcome by the hospital staff. After discharge, hospitals often supervise the follow-up of patients. This is sometimes criticized by G.P.s as being unnecessary, but often it is to the patient's benefit, because he needs both specialist skills and hospital environment. The G.P. has a justifiable grievance, however, in that the hospital does not always provide him with sufficient information of the patient's condition or progress. [13] This is absolutely essential for continuity as well as courtesy, but it by no means always happens.

The myth of continuity of care is most apparent for those patients who require repeated periods of hospital treatment. With the present tripartite system, the G.P., the hospital, and the local authority are each responsible for providing separate segments of a service that ought rationally to be a whole. Communications between these three sectors are minimal, and, indeed, there are no organized channels of communication. Forsyth and Logan in their study entitled *The Demand for Medical Care* [14] state that it is at the point of integration between the hospital and the domiciliary services where the N.H.S. is most unsuccessful. The G.P. is just not in the position, with the present administrative set-up, to provide continuous personal supervision of his patients during periods of sickness.

A special problem in general practice is the number of patients whose complaints are largely emotional or psychological in origin. Very few G.P.s have been trained to cope with the task of detecting these. Medical students are taught comparatively little psychiatry, and much of what is taught concerns only the severe psychotic forms of illness. This may well explain the readiness of many G.P.s to label apparently unnecessary calls from patients as trivial. Some of these patients could probably be treated adequately by a suitably trained G.P., but successful psychotherapy requires a great deal of time; more than a patient can expect from doctors under the present system.

The description of these darker features of general practice confirms the view that the most serious problems are not those related to remuneration, although this is the aspect which has tended to receive most attention. More important, in fact, are problems which arise from the conditions of service and the demands of the role itself. Only by the most earnest endeavours can the conscientious doctor overcome the obstacles to good medical practice which are features of the present organization of medical care. The good G.P., and there are many of these, is well aware of the deficiencies in the care which he can at present provide in Britain.

Under the present system there are many barriers to competence, other than those produced by the tripartite administration, which account in part of these deficiencies. G.P.s are overworked, not necessarily with legitimate medical affairs, but with administrative duties which should be handled by secretarial assistants. The G.P. often does not have the time to make the necessary preliminary examinations. Only 30 per cent of G.P.s have effective secretarial help, and without this adequate note-taking is hardly feasible. [15] These problems can best be solved only within the context of major administrative reform, as recognized in the *B.M.J.* [16] editorial entitled "General Practice Outmoded."

The G.P.'s dilemma has been pithily summarized by Dr. Richard Scott, the first British Professor of General Practice, as problems of time, tools, and training. It is said, therefore, that the way to improve general practice is to provide the doctor with efficient and pleasant premises, with access to modern diagnostic and therapeutic equipment, and to save the G.P.'s time by using non-medical colleagues for non-medical jobs. In addition it is suggested that we should alter medical education so as to train the doctor specifically for general practice rather than to half-train him in a number of specialities as at present.

The problem of premises is now being tackled by granting loans to groups of doctors, by building health centres, and by allowing the G.P.s to use local authority clinic buildings. Increased expense allowances for secretarial help and the development of training courses for secretary–receptionists should improve the administration of practices. Attachment or alternative schemes of liaison with community nurses should provide more nursing help for the doctor, more satisfying work for the nurse, and a better service to the patient. Attachment schemes for health visitors would provide for the G.P. a close link with workers who have training in both health education and social work.

An important aspect of current planning for general practice is to reduce, if not abolish, isolated practice. The doctor, like other professionals, needs the stimulation of his colleagues to encourage him to maintain high standards of work. Grouping of practitioners also makes it much easier to arrange cover for holidays and study. In addition, since a group practice serves a larger population than the single G.P., the work can be shared more easily with paramedical workers such as nurses, social workers, technicians, receptionists, and secretaries. In some places there are plans to bring the G.P. into closer contact with the hospitals, partly by giving him sessions of hospital employment and partly by encouraging him to visit hospitals to see patients and attend meetings.

Various suggestions have been made about ways to improve the initial training and postgraduate education of the G.P. Medical education is at present confined largely to hospital experience, and this is now recognized as being a serious imbalance. In addition there is little opportunity or incentive for G.P.s to continue their education so that they keep up with advances in medical techniques and treatment. Schemes have been suggested for re-designing undergraduate and postgraduate training for those who will go into general practice and for paid leave or other incentives to encourage doctors to attend refresher courses regularly.

These changes would undoubtedly improve matters. The question is whether they would be sufficient, and whether they make sense in relation to the planning of other parts of the health service. We also need to consider whether there have been advances in medical technology and general social changes which explain why other industrial countries, as politically different as the U.S.A., the U.S.S.R. and the Scandinavian countries, have sharply reduced or abolished, in urban areas, general practice as we know it in this country. The essence of present-day thinking, such as that in the Gillie Report, is that we must and can have family doctors who are competent as primary diagnosticians for all age groups and conditions, and who will work from independent centres, largely separate from the other health services.

These assumptions can be called in question and there are many points at which such a plan must inevitably falter.

In the first place, all are agreed that the G.P. must be allowed increased access to diagnostic facilities and that it is essential that he learns to make greater use of these. Basic radiological and pathological tests should be readily available, and he should be able to refer, with ease, patients who require more specialized tests to the appropriate consultant. Modern diagnostic equipment is usually both expensive and unsuitable for transport, and only a very small proportion could be widely dispersed to G.P. surgeries or health centres. Under the present system the G.P. will have to make use of hospital facilities, and therefore in this context it is necessary to examine the implications of the hospital plan for domiciliary medical practice. [17]

The district general hospitals, of the 1962 Hospital Plan, were originally intended to have 600–800 beds and to serve a population of 100,000–150,000. Subsequent statements have suggested that the size will increase rather than decrease. Even in an area of fairly high population density of 4000 per square mile, this could mean that one hospital would have to cover an area up to about 3 miles in radius. The larger the population that we make our hospitals cover, therefore, the harder we make it for domiciliary doctors and their patients to reach diagnostic equipment.

There is evidence that distance plays an important part in determining how much use G.P.s are likely to make of open access to hospital facilities. [18] There is no cognizance of the problem in the hospital plan, no intention to build diagnostic centres which would bridge the gap, and insufficient capital laid aside for the expansion of diagnostic aids which such open access would entail.

This is hardly surprising. The hospital plan was not drawn up with the primary aim of integrating the three arms of the health service. Considerations of size of hospital and the physical extent of its catchment area were not viewed from the standpoint of the G.P., or projected improvements in domiciliary care largely, again, because of the strict division of responsibility between the

Regional Board and the Executive Council, even at Ministry planning level. Consequently, the conventional solutions to the G.P.'s problem, which consist simply of grafting additions on to the existing hospital plan, are unlikely to be adequate. The G.P. is justifiably dissatisfied with this kind of piece-meal solution, where his particular needs have not been fully considered. The G.P. deals with over 90 per cent of all illnesses which are treated by doctors, [19] and his position deserves more careful attention when new services are planned.

As medical knowledge and skills have become more complex, there has been a steady separation of specialist groups from the generalist types of doctor. Indeed, medicine is a good illustration of the economic theory that increasing complexity necessitates a division of labour. The G.P. in Britain has seen less change in the organization of medical practice than countries which do not have our kind of administrative stability. A generalist was retained in the front-line of the Service and although in theory it is attractive to have a doctor who combines competence in several specialities, we have seen that for one reason or another this concept does not seem to be working well. It is quite unrealistic to demand from one man a high level of recognizing illness and in the knowledge of an intricate array of diagnostic aids and therapy for the full spectrum of disease. This is an important reason why other countries have organized primary medical care around teams of specialists, although not always with complete success. In particular, if we are to develop the front-line doctor as the king-pin in preventive medicine, which requires the early recognition of symptoms that are slight or indefinite, one must somehow allow the doctor to deepen his knowledge without losing the advantage of the whole-body, whole-person approach, which the narrow organ-specialist finds difficult.

Most orthodox solutions contain within them the inference that to improve G.P. competence, it is necessary to reduce the size of his list. While it may be true that a case load of 3000 and more is too great a burden for one man to carry, if the present system is maintained there could be grave consequences for the doctor's competence in reducing the size of population for which he is responsible. For many serious conditions, the incidence is low, and to reduce the size of the G.P.'s list will lessen still further his experience in meeting these conditions and hence his ability to recognize them. For example, bronchiolitis in young children is not very common, but it can be fatal if it is not treated correctly. It is dangerous, therefore, if G.P.s do not encounter it sufficiently often to be able to diagnose it in the early stages. Sir Dugald Baird has pointed out that in large towns, G.P.s are responsible for only about half the deliveries in their practices, and that these deliveries are selected for their expected normality. "He has therefore little experience of abnormal midwifery, and so cannot help the experienced midwife when she is in difficulties."[20] The term "family doctor" has become very popular with G.P.s. Some go so far as to describe the G.P. as a "specialist in family medicine". When, however, these doctors describe the work and training of the family doctor, it is clear that they are describing doctors who are partially trained in a number of specialities. Fox[21] in suggesting an alternative to the term for G.P.s, namely "personal doctor", drew attention to the fact that not all members of families wish to have the same doctor. Two recent studies of urban practice showed that no less than 20 per cent of the members of families chose to register with different doctors.[22, 23] Adolescents, for example, frequently prefer not to use the family practitioner. Then, too, we should remember the large proportion of the population that does not conform to the pattern of the nuclear family, single people and the widowed, for example. It may not be necessary to maintain the present concept of the family doctor in order to ensure that all patients have a personal doctor. We have already cited instances to illustrate that one of the most important functions of the personal doctor, to provide continuity of care, is often impossible in any case with the present system. There are many other areas where fragmentation of services exist—e.g. maternity care, now split between the G.P., the hospital, and the local authority clinic, and the health of school-children which is catered for in part by the G.P., with assistance from the hospital specialists, and in part by the school health services of the local authority. If the child suffers from an emotional disorder, yet another individual—the education authority's educational psychologist—will be called upon. Simply tinkering with the present services, without a radical plan to integrate the various segments, cannot be expected to provide a satisfactory solution to this state of affairs.

Surely the value of the concept of a family doctor lies particularly in the understanding of the interactions of mothers and young children and in seeing the need for continuity of medical care. Co-operation between doctors could cover the former problem, while continuity of care must be achieved by far-reaching changes in the administrative organization and the siting of services. In an industrial society which is increasingly mobile, we surely have to plan for continuity of care to be incorporated into the health service by means other than relying on the memory and resources of one doctor. Even under ideal conditions none of us can expect more than 40 years' care from an individual doctor, and it is usually considerably less.

Adequate medical records and modern data processing could give us good family and personal medical histories as they have been doing in Denmark for a number of years. The advantages offered by the automation of medical records, and the changes which such methods are likely to necessitate in the development and organization of the health services, have clearly not been considered so far in the plans to extend the Service. These methods need not be regarded as something which will materialize only in the distant future. In America much research has been devoted to their development, and in our own country some progress has been made already in the application of the computer to medical problems. West Sussex, for example, has been operating a highly successful computer control of immunization for several years.

Data-processing equipment, whether punched cards or computers, needs larger numbers for efficient use than could be provided by the patients of a few G.P.s lists. By dealing with large groups of patients we could, however, easily provide doctors with many statistical analyses which would aid them in their work, and, incidentally, remove much of the tedium associated with good record keeping as well as improving efficiency. In addition an important new development in medical care is the extension of the use of screening tests for signs of early illness. Cervical smear examinations are a well-known example. These tests are most effectively used if they are carried out on the groups most at risk. Again, the organization of such programmes will be greatly helped if records are handled by machine. As screening tests develop, we can therefore expect to see the administration of such programmes being conducted on large rather than small groups of the population. In this case they are unlikely to be examinations that the individual G.P. can organize. Data-processing could be a responsibility of the present or enlarged executive councils, if suitably equipped. But should we not consider rationalizing our various administrative boundaries for health, so as to facilitate this kind of development? In this field, yet again, we see the benefits of a fully integrated service. Resolution of the tripartite system would allow such rationalization.

CHAPTER 4

The Failure of the Tripartite Administration

WITHIN the first 10 years of the inception of the National Health Service, representations on the tripartite scheme were received by the Guillebaud Committee, which had been set up in 1953, to review the cost of the Service and to give advice on its organization. The committee received evidence on the need to unify the three branches of the Service, and, according to its authors, the evidence advocated either one new statutory body for all three, or the return to local authorities of hospitals, or the transfer of general practitioner services to regional hospital boards. In its report in 1956, the committee advised the Minister of Health against all-purpose authorities because of the importance they attached to local authority domiciliary services and the signs they detected that the authorities had begun to make the best use of the administrative machinery.

It is unfortunate that the years following the committee's report have not altogether confirmed their confidence in local authority services. Although individual examples of failures by local authorities and hospitals may be numerous, we do not propose to discuss these, in this context, but to consider the wider problem of the failure of the tripartite services to complement each other.

It would be wrong to suggest that there is complete chaos and failure to liaise within the present structure. Often there is a feeling of helplessness that results in respective authorities accepting limitations, and, in true British spirit, working round them. Limitations thus become "occupational hazards". One can imagine this being the reaction of one teaching hospital specialist who wrote to *The Guardian* about his experiences in "attempting and, more often than not, failing, in the provision of home helps for patients being discharged from hospitals into areas controlled by eight or nine county or London Boroughs". [1] One cannot blame staff for giving up the fight against such an octopus. Conversely, the boroughs in question might also feel critical of the hospitals for their admission policies, and in particular for their apparently abrupt decision to discharge patients in some cases.

Liaison, where it is achieved, tends to be cumbersome and often slightly self-conscious. In Liverpool, for example, liaison has been achieved between the hospital departments, and local authority welfare, health, and works departments (four in all) in the treatment of patients at home requiring kidney dialysis. This link, at the hospital staffs' request, could only be achieved, in fact, under a clause in the National Assistance Act. The achievement is regarded as a triumph, as indeed it is given the complications of the present system, but it should not be necessary to go to such lengths to provide an essential service.

G.P.s do not have officially defined catchment areas for their patients, hence where other services are organized with definite geographic boundaries, G.P.s often have to deal with several different authorities for the same service. This particularly affects, for instance, local health services, which include home nurses, health visitors, domiciliary midwives, mental health officers, public health inspectors, and local authority welfare and social services, which include welfare officers, welfare accommodation, and child care in relation to fostering and adoption.

This problem is particularly troublesome in the Greater London area, but also significantly affects general practitioners working in county boroughs. County boroughs are responsible for about a third of the population, and a common problem is that G.P.s have some patients in a county borough and some in the surrounding county. Thus if a patient needs a midwife in the home, a different administration deals with the service if the patient is a county rather than a county borough resident.

This may seem to be a trivial problem, since G.P.s who have been working in an area for some time learn where the local government boundaries run, and therefore they know which service to contact. But there is considerable evidence that G.P.s are not mobilizing health and social services adequately for their patients (and themselves) and that this is at least partly due to the complexity of organization of local services. Even the most obvious service which G.P.s should know and use well, home nursing, has recently been surveyed by the Queen's Institute of District Nursing (*Feeling the Pulse*) and an appalling lack of communication with doctors was demonstrated.

Although G.P.s send only about 10 per cent of their patients for hospital services, this group includes most of the seriously ill. Both the out-patient and in-patient services of local hospitals are continuously involved in the transfer of patients to and from G.P.s' care. Despite the obvious natural interrelation of services, the management structure of hospital services at regional and local levels has an inadequate representation of G.P.s—hence G.P.s' frequent complaints about the organization of local hospital diagnostic, clinical, and emergency services.

Family planning and occupational health services are important examples of services which are impoverished and which are organized mainly quite separately from the N.H.S. services. These considerations give practitioners further problems in mobilizing services for their patients.

Over the past 10 years in Britain, mainly through the development of attachment schemes in which local authority nursing and related services are organized on a practice rather than a geographical basis, it has been demonstrated that easier and effective work can be carried out in community health teams. With local and integrated organization of services, G.P.s would have much more chance of working in teams and being properly equipped for their task. Expensive, but only partly used local authority clinics, separate from makeshift G.P.'s surgeries and inadequately linked to local hospital clinics and services would become less common since the planning of buildings and facilities would be integrated.

The confusion which arises as a result of the proliferation of administrative boundaries and the overlap of responsibilities is admirably illustrated by the child guidance services. Initially divided before the Second World War into educational and psychiatric spheres, the service has never achieved a satisfactory degree of unification. At that time it was considered that the local authority clinics need deal only with educational problems and children needing psychiatric treatment should be referred to hospital clinics. In 1955 the Underwood Committee on Maladjusted Children reported that for hospitals and local education authorities to plan in isolation was not in the best interests of the children, and urged the creation of joint clinics headed by a psychiatrist with educational psychiatrists as part of his team. [2] The administrative control would, however, be under the principal school medical officer. Following a joint circular by the Ministries of Education and Health in 1959, this has become the pattern. At clinic levels most reports indicate that the team concept is working well, but discussion on the overall organization has continued. Some expert observers urge hospital control entirely, particularly in view of the increasing awareness of the need for institutional backing. There is in all parts of the country a serious lack of psychiatric in-patient facilities for adolescents and children. Others hold that child guidance clinics must remain as part of the educational service. In 1959 the Association of Education Committees went on record as saying "the great majority of cases which come within the child guidance service do not require psychiatric treatment, and are best dealt with by a competent educational psychologist working in conjunction with social workers and teaching staff, and using the normal facilities of the school health service". [3] Such remarks are a classic statement of vested interests, and apparently disregard such things as bedwetting, maladjustment, and autism in children, recognizing only reading difficulties and educational backwardness as major problems. An example of the present confusion with regard to this service is offered in one rural area where the organization is as follows. In this county the Child Guidance Service is provided by the county council Health and Education Departments, with part-time consultant psychiatrists appointed by the regional hospital board. The major population in the particular rural area is a market town which is 25 miles away from the Child Guidance Clinic, to which there is poor public transport access. Only 15 miles away is a large town, in a different county and with a hospital-based Child Guidance Clinic. Public transport links with this town are good and consequently G.P.s in the market town tend to refer children to this clinic. Being in a different county the latter clinic is not served by the same school psychological service as the market town. School referrals are therefore rarely made. A satellite clinic was established by the county council in the market town some years ago which produced a flow of referrals. However, subsequently the county council reorganized its divisional administrative boundaries. The market town passed into another area, and a new clinic for the town was set up 20 miles away, again with poor access. So far the satellite clinic has not been re-established and the referral rate has again dropped to its former level.

The failure to recognize social factors in contemporary society and to plan accordingly is shown in present-day arrangements for the care of the elderly. Townsend and Wedderburn foresee the need for three- to fourfold increase in domiciliary care for the aged in their book *The Aged in the Welfare State* (1965). In the past elderly relatives were cared for largely by their relatives, but this is becoming less common, partly because of housing shortages and the fact that young families often move out to new towns or housing estates and live at some distance from their ageing relatives.

This means that we must increase domiciliary and local welfare services for the elderly which, we hope, would produce a corresponding reduction in the demand for residential homes. Townsend has calculated that over half of the present residents in such institutions could stay in their own homes if more adequate and flexible domiciliary care were available. It has also been shown that less than a third of the residents want to stay permanently in institutions. At the same time, the last few years has seen an increasing emphasis on short-stay units, with a view to patients returning to their own homes—thereby imposing yet further demands upon the already strained local authority services.

Modern thinking of a similar kind about community care for children, mentally ill and severely subnormal, all point to the need for an expansion of work which cannot be successfully achieved when directed, as at present, by fragmented authorities. Small local government areas, a multiplication of departments, diffident leadership, all combine to preclude communication and the discussion of new techniques in treatment, building, staffing, or administration. The necessity for overall planning demands a formal, unified structure.

It is in the publication of the local authorities' 10-year Health and Welfare Plan that the evidence is most readily found that local authority services are not functioning satisfactorily. The plan, published in 1963 [4] (and later revised) [5] showed that there will still be enormous differences between the services provided in different areas. The Ministry of Health, in evidence to the Royal Commission on Local Government, [6] optimistically state that the two plans show that local authority services are in a "state of active growth", although later they admit that "performance varies very greatly . . . no authority yet provides a uniformly good and adequate service over the whole range". A "state of active growth" is no doubt reflected by the increasing cost of local authority services, and it is true that they have risen proportionately faster than that of the health service as a whole. Nevertheless, the average health and welfare expenditure in 1965 varied from £3. 1s. 2d. per head in Cardiganshire to £1 3s. 0d. in Northampton, while the national average was £1. 17s. 4d.

In the field of mental health, there has been, ever since the operation on the 1959 Mental Health Act [7] considerable concern at the level of community provision by local authorities, and in 1963 a report on the subject by P.E.P. [8] concluded that: "if community care is to expand, it is of the utmost importance that existing administrative barriers should not be allowed to impede the development of co-ordinated psychiatric services." The sort of integration needed is more fundamental than that achieved simply by operating joint case-conferences. Shortcomings of community health services have an immediate effect on increasing the demand for hospital beds, but as a result of the present administrative and financial structure, it is hardly surprising to find that many local authorities do not accept their responsibilities in this matter. It is disappointing to find the Ministry of Health stating in 1967 that "no authority is yet providing a completely comprehensive service, and in many areas some part of the services needed are completely lacking" (*ibid.*). All in all it is hard to escape the conclusion that the variation in local authority services will hardly be less striking in 1972 as a result of the plans submitted in 1962, for only four local authorities will be providing the minimum requirements.

The policies adopted by the hospital service likewise have repercussions over the provision and administration of such things as local maternity services. In some areas medical policy allows for the early discharge of mothers, in others not: in either case the local authority has to fit as best it can in the provision of its own domiciliary care. The National Birthday Fund [9] shows some evidence of infant mortality and illnesses occurring because staff in each branch of the tripartite structure thinks one of the other sections has dealt with a particular test or examination. The standards of service are uneven between areas, and most districts are forced to have priorities governing hospital admissions. The indications here point to the need for one senior consultant responsible for all aspects and standards of the service. This system has, in effect, been established in Aberdeen, where an outstanding record in maternal care has been established.

In the context of domiciliary after-care, it is interesting to note a recent proposal by the Radcliffe Infirmary to establish a domiciliary nursing scheme for after-care of some patients, which reveals yet another anomaly in the tripartite structure. For minor operations such as varicose veins or hernias, it is proposed to discharge patients to their homes the day after the operation, and teams of nurses from the Infirmary will help G.P.s and district nurses in their after-care. Social workers and home helps will also be part of the domiciliary team. Since such patients frequently stay in hospital for up to a fortnight at present, this scheme will allow a much more rapid turn-over of beds and help reduce waiting lists for these operations. However, the hospital will have to raise privately about £7000 to initiate this project because the Ministry of Health is not allowed to give grants for this type of work to hospitals. It is possible to give such grants to a local authority, however, so if the scheme can be launched—with private funds—the Minister will then provide money through this source to keep the scheme in operation, although he has promised to do so for only one year. [10]

The required expansion of services, both institutional and community, calls for a staffing policy in the light of present-day factors and skills in planning and building which can only be achieved by an integrated approach. There are already acute staffing difficulties in all three sectors of the health service. National manpower planners predict a tightly stretched position until 1980. During this time, assuming that hospitals go on treating an ever-increasing number of patients, extra hospital staff will be wanted. Estimates vary, but one is that an additional 700,000 hospital staff will be required, and the local authority plan anticipated that by 1972 an additional 120,000 will be required by them to implement the proposals.

At the present time, however, there are already grave shortages of staff—including nurses and doctors, who require years of training, and therefore cannot be readily obtained even in an era of high unemployment. The shortage of medical staff, which resulted from the 10 per cent cut in 1957 of the numbers admitted to medical schools, is now being slowly rectified, but it must be remembered that it takes 15 years to produce a fully qualified medical specialist. The shortage of nurses seems unavoidable as the 1961 census showed a continuation of the steady decline in the proportion of single women in the age group 20–34. The shortage of social workers in local authority employment is acute now, with 2487 child care officers in post at 31 March 1966, and an anticipated requirement of 4190 by the end of 1968. Meanwhile it is hoped that the annual number qualifying will rise from 280 in 1966 to 675 by 1969. In all these fields recruits must, therefore, be won from other professional careers open to women, and clearly there is a need for some kind of overall "social service manpower" planning. Within the present tripartite system, particularly with some sectors relying heavily on voluntary committees and local councillors, it is impossible to provide the sort of strong central direction needed to avoid delay, overlapping, and wastage of a scarce national resource.

The system of ten-year plans, published for both local authority services and hospitals, was an attempt to achieve a unity of purpose at local level, although the fact that hospital catchment areas do not relate to local authority boundaries hinders this intention. While all such attempts to achieve integration are laudable, there are at present good reasons why we should consider how the health service could be radically altered and integrated under one control. Since the existing structure can be seen as ineffective, the time is opportune for a full reorganization, in that local government is under review by a royal commission, and currently a large-scale modernization and replanning of hospitals is taking place at an overall cost of £800 million by 1972.

"A piece of administrative machinery, the ideas of which belong to the age of Victoria" is how the organization of the N.H.S. has been described. It is salutory to consider again what the sum total of the parts amount to: 15 regional hospital boards, 336 hospital management committees, 134 executive councils controlling the affairs of 20,000 G.P.s, and 174 local health authorities. The question has been posed as to how far this structure is best suited to present-day needs in the light of experience up to the present and of more recent developments; How adequately does it reflect new concepts in government? How far can the hospital service develop in isolation from social planning? It is impossible to avoid a negative answer.*

---

* We have included in Appendix II some typical case-histories which illustrate the effects of the tripartite division on individuals.

CHAPTER 5

The Failure of Tripartite in Relation to the Mental Health Services

AT PRESENT the mental health services are subject to the same divisive administrative structure as the general medical services. In addition, despite Ministry intentions and the specific aim of the Mental Health Act of 1959, the mental health services are still largely separate from other branches of medicine. In-patient services continue to be based primarily on the large comprehensive psychiatric hospitals, which means that hospitals for the mentally ill and the mentally sub-normal are usually specialist hospitals which do not admit non-psychiatric patients; each type of hospital tends to take patients of all ages and all categories of disorder, and provides both short-stay and long-stay care in one hospital unit. Hospitals aim to provide for all the clinical, residential, and training needs of their patients. Patients in the community are cared for by the local health authority mental health services, which aim to provide for the welfare and training needs of patients living at home. The medical treatment of patients living at home is shared between some combination of the local authority medical officers for mental health, the G.P., and hospital psychiatrists working in out-patient departments. Patients requiring detailed assessment or intensive clinical care are referred to hospital, together with the majority of patients requiring residential care whether this is for medical or social reasons.

At the inception of the N.H.S. in 1946, the whole status of the mentally disordered,* their treatment, and prognosis was very

* The terminology used here and in Chapter 10 will be that of the Mental Health Act of 1959, which treats separately the mentally ill and the mentally sub-normal, and uses the term "mentally disordered" when referring to both types of patient.

different from now, although to some extent the process of change had already begun in the most progressive hospitals. Consequently, at that time, perhaps not surprisingly, the undesirability of the tripartite system for the care of the mentally disordered was not fully recognized.

Even in 1946 there were relatively few effective clinical treatments for the mentally ill in general use. For the mentally subnormal there was little knowledge of their capacity to learn or develop new skills. There was a great deal of public apprehension concerning the mentally disordered with a consequent emphasis on custodial care rather than on treatment or rehabilitation.

The mentally disordered in hospital were legally different from other patients in that most were detained by a legal order and were usually housed, by law, in hospitals caring only for psychiatric cases. This applied particularly to the mentally sub-normal who officially had no informal in-patient status until 1952 and could not be hospitalized except under a legal order and in designated institutions. Both for the mentally ill and the mentally sub-normal there was little appreciation or recognition that the majority of patients were capable of doing useful work and being at least semi-independent. In addition, there was little awareness of the damaging effect on patient behaviour of a poor hospital social environment or the reality of the syndrome of institutionalization.

As a result of these facts, care for the mentally disordered was largely equated with rigid custodial hospital care. There was little provision for care within the community and it was assumed that most of such patients needed hospital admission, if not immediately, then in the long run. In practice, even at that time, about half the mentally sub-normal and perhaps a quarter of the mentally ill were kept at home receiving few, if any, services, and simply cared for by their families. It was a common assumption, however, even by doctors, that all these patients ought to be in hospital and that community care was only second best. Once patients were admitted to hospital it was difficult to get them out again, particularly for the majority who were admitted on a legal order. In any case, treatment in hospital was such that commonly patients did not improve sufficiently to warrant any efforts to place them back in the community.

Under these circumstances, the strict division between community and hospital services did not seem inappropriate; according to the prevailing attitudes of most doctors and of the public, the mentally disordered would, and should, be removed from the community and cared for indefinitely in discreetly distant suburbs. Since 1946, however, there has been a revolution in the Anglo-Saxon countries, and particularly in England, in public and medical attitudes to mental illness, and in this context the present administrative divisions are quite anachronistic.

This revolution began with the introduction of the "open-door" policy and the idea of the mental hospital as a therapeutic community in which all types of staff were important members of the treatment programme, and where patients were encouraged to develop independence as far as this was possible. This pattern of care had been in existence for many years, of course, in the most progressive hospitals, but it was not until after the introduction of the N.H.S. that such policies were extensively practised. During the 1950's also, a number of new drugs and other physical treatments were developed which resulted in improved prognosis for the mentally ill. More important, perhaps, was the psychological effect, particularly on staff but also on patients, of reassigning large groups of patients into the "treatable" category who were formerly regarded as "untreatable". This applied particularly to schizophrenic patients who in 1946 formed the majority of patients resident in mental hospitals. In addition, these treatments reduced the distinction between the mentally ill and the physically ill, since from the point of view of medical treatment, both now could be regarded as essentially similar.

At the same time, other important social changes were occurring. It gradually became recognized that many more patients could be returned to the community, if on a somewhat precarious basis. This meant that rehabilitation programmes became more important in treating patients, and also the role of the psychiatric social worker achieved a new significance. It also became apparent that even patients who were unable to return home were capable of doing useful work and that this in itself helped the patient to become less disturbed and withdrawn. The extension of training in hospitals for the mentally sub-normal showed that even low-grade patients were capable of coping satisfactorily with simple production line industrial tasks which were both profitable and gave patients a new status which improved their whole well-being. [1, 2] Research into social organization in hospitals revealed that this could be crucial in determining patient prognosis. Hospitals where patients were given more independence, more privacy, and more status, even in simple things like whether they were allowed to wear their own clothes and have a locker to keep private possessions, showed a much lower percentage of seriously disturbed patients than hospitals where this was not the case. [3] Investigations into factors such as the patient's family relationships and employment opportunities related to re-admission rates, have also shown the great importance of community social factors on the degree of disturbance and future prognosis. [4, 5] Although many patients improve greatly when treated within the community, because of these factors some patients who are discharged do break down after a period of trial at home and have to be re-admitted to hospital for another spell of treatment.

As a result of these changes the whole pattern of treatment and prognosis for the mentally ill and for the mentally sub-normal is now very different to that which was common practice in 1946. The fact that it is recognized that many patients respond better to treatment within the community than if they remain in hospital, has coincided with an increasing awareness of community responsibility for the sick and underprivileged. The change in legal status which resulted from the 1959 Mental Health Act facilitated the development of new patterns of care, since it became possible for patients to receive short periods of hospital treatment, on the same basis as the physically ill, and made it feasible for general hospitals to extend or develop psychiatric units. At the same time, the improvement in the control and treatment of children's infectious diseases emptied wards in many paediatric hospitals which could be utilized for sub-normal children requiring short periods of hospital care. Research into the causes of some forms of subnormality have suggested preventive measures which may effect the incidence of some conditions, and treatment measures, both surgical and medical, which may limit the extent of damage to brain tissue. Again, the distinction between psychiatry and general medicine is therefore declining since it is apparent that the effectiveness of the general medical services, particularly the maternity services, is very closely related to the incidence of severe subnormality, and that babies who are born with damage to the nervous system can often be treated with, at least, limited success by the normal paediatric and orthopaedic services.

These changes are not perhaps operating so thoroughly as one would like. But the revolution has at least begun and has made obsolete the rigid distinction between community services, preventive measures, and hospital care, and also the prevailing tendency which still exists to separate the mental health services from general medicine. It is now being realized that these services are by nature mutually interdependent, but it is difficult and sometimes impossible to operate them as such within the present administrative framework. Logically, therefore, it would be more effective to organize the mental health services under a unified administration, and to ally them more closely with the other medical services.

In the first place, treatment for the psychoses now usually follows a pattern of alternating periods of in-patient and out-patient treatment, and continuity of care is at present disrupted by changes in personnel as the patient moves between administrative boundaries. At present the hospital frequently discharges patients without adequate knowledge of the family situation or the possibilities of community support. Many hospitals do not have an adequate staff of psychiatric social workers, but even if they do, the hospital social worker does not have sufficient opportunity to observe the patient in his home environment although this is essential to a proper assessment of the situation. This problem is magnified when hospitals are situated outside the main urban centres or even outside the catchment area which they serve, which is often the case.

Hospital siting is itself a very important aspect of care. Mental hospitals are not at present sited in relation to local needs, and in the Metropolitan area, in particular, they are so frequently found outside the main conurbation that a ring of institutions has developed round London, fondly known as the "lunatic fringe". This state of affairs makes complete nonsense of the idea of community integration. In the long term these hospitals will have to be abandoned, not only because they are based too far away from the urban centres, but also because the buildings are old and have inadequate facilities. Hospital re-building which is now being planned, however, should not occur in isolation from plans for developing residential and other facilities in the community. At present there is little joint consultation between the hospital and the local authority on this point, although inevitably their functions overlap. However, hospitals cannot be evacuated overnight, and meanwhile the full integration of community and hospital social work is the only way to make continuity of care a feasible target. Under the present circumstances contacts between hospital psychiatric social workers and local authority workers cannot be very effective, and hospital social workers often have a poor understanding or knowledge of the local employment opportunities for the patients they help to discharge.

Conversely, domiciliary workers, including G.P.s who have to take over the care of the patient on discharge, do not have direct access to his hospital records or those who treated him in hospital. In consequence they are often inadequately informed about his clinical condition, or the likelihood of relapse. On discharge, the patient becomes the medical responsibility of the G.P. who may take over drug treatment. However, most G.P.s have a meagre knowledge of psychiatry and of psychiatric drugs, especially those trained before the 1950's. They are rarely competent to supervise the patient without some guidance from the specialist, but this is not easily achieved within the present framework, especially if the psychiatric hospital is situated at a distance from the patient's home. If the patient has been treated in a psychiatric unit from the general hospital, he may attend the out-patient department and receive his drugs from the hospital dispensary. This will perhaps ensure better supervision, but medical responsibility is then divided between the hospital psychiatrist and the G.P. and the latter is still expected to provide 24 hour cover for this patient as for all others in his practice. If a crisis occurs at night or over the week-end, the G.P. may be called in, but having little knowledge of the patient's general condition he may not be able to act effectively. There is also poor contact between the G.P. and the local authority workers. This leaves the G.P. in the very ambiguous position of having responsibility without adequate knowledge of the treatment pattern decided upon by the hospital or the local authority, which may in fact differ in many respects. It is hardly surprising that G.P.s feel that they are underrated by the psychiatric hospitals and the local health authority mental health department.

Local authority social workers, the mental welfare officers, who normally have to cope with the day-to-day problems of management of the discharged patient and his family, also have poor contacts with the hospitals. The mental welfare officer may not even agree that the family is capable of receiving the patient home, or at any rate that it could do so only if support could be given in terms of workshop or employment facilities which may not be available at the time of discharge.

Many patients are not considered suitable by the hospital as long-term residents and quite rightly so, since they would be capable of living or working in the community, but only with a battery of community services. Hospitals regard the latter as the responsibility of the local authority and discharge the patient on this assumption. The local authority simply may not be capable of providing these services, however, particularly if the patient's family is not able to receive him home. Hospitals have traditionally provided both clinical treatment and long-term residential accommodation, and it is difficult for everyone concerned to accept that these functions can be separated. The division of financial and administrative responsibility between the regional hospital board and the local health authority does nothing to aid in this respect. Rehabilitation requires a flexible system of half-way houses with ease of access between these, together with permanent residential care for patients who cannot live at home or in lodgings. The Ministry has informed local authorities that they should provide hostel accommodation for psychiatric patients. Local authorities are often prepared to build hostels for short-term care, but long-term care, traditionally the function of the hospitals, they are reluctant to provide since they regard the chronic sick as the financial responsibility of the regional hospital board. Even if they do recognize their new role with respect to long-term accommodation, many authorities are too small or too poor to finance these. The regional boards, on the other hand, tend to regard hostel provision as the function of the local authority, and, in any case, hospitals are often themselves inappropriately sited to provide hostel care if patients are to work or mix with freedom in the community.

As a result, hostels are now provided both by hospitals and the local authority on a very haphazard basis, and no one is clear who should be providing what kind of hostel service. Plans rarely exist between regional hospital board and local health authorities to co-ordinate development of hostels in a particular area or to decide what kinds of patients they are designed for. In consequence some areas are over-supplied with short-term hostels and have vacant places because local authorities refuse to accept patients who may prove to be long-term residents. Yet it seems that the demand for long-term accommodation is much greater than for short-term care, and local health authorities constantly complain about their hostels becoming silted up. Consequently, very few areas have sufficient long-term hostels, sited within the community, so that suitable patients can work in normal jobs.

With regard to the training of patients, the concept of rehabilitation would again imply the need for a series of graded workshops through which patients could progress, from a completely sheltered environment to a factory-simulated environment as a preparation for return to normal working conditions. Patients may need retraining for new jobs since their former occupations may no longer be suitable. At present both hospitals and local authorities attempt to provide some training schemes and workshops. For some types of patient, for example, the mentally sub-normal child, the local authority services are fairly efficient, at least in large urban centres. By contrast, hospital training centres for sub-normal children are on the whole poor. [6] A few outstanding local authorities and hospitals have good training schemes for adults, but usually these are highly inadequate.

One of the main problems here is the quite separate issue that the health services should not be expected to provide training, which is the proper function of the Education Department and of the Ministry of Labour. Hospitals, in particular, especially if they are not very progressive in their outlook, do not have the orientation necessary to provide good training facilities. Traditionally, hospitals are organized to care and protect patients. Education and training require the opposite approach, i.e. to encourage patients to become independent and if necessary to push them into doing this. "Total push" procedures are common in the best mental hospitals where patients are simply not allowed to stagnate, but it requires a revolution in attitude on the part of hospital staff to accept that this is both good and necessary.

There is also no logical reason why training should be sited within hospitals at all, for those many patients who are capable of catching a bus to school or work. Many patients in hospital are precisely the same in condition and mental state as others who live at home, and work or train in the community. To keep such patients for 24 hours a day within the hospital confines does not aid their return to normal life. In fact, both community-based and hospital-based patients have exactly the same needs with regard to training and should benefit if in-patient and out-patient training services were co-ordinated to give some rational sequence of care.

Possibly the main barrier to developing a good national system of community services at present is the fact that the local health authorities differ very markedly in size, that is in area, population or income. To provide an adequate service is more costly than many local authorities can afford. In addition, the expense of the wide range of services necessary can only be justified if there are a sufficient number of patients to make use of them, and so are prohibitive for authorities with a small population or county boroughs where the population is widely scattered. It is no accident that those authorities which have the best reputation are frequently those which are relatively large in population or in income. One medical sociologist has argued that with the N.H.S. we have created, not a welfare state, but a series of welfare areas, because the differences are so great between areas in the welfare services they can provide. [7] If hospital and community services were financed by a single authority, services could be planned to meet local needs without relying on local financial resources and there could be a sharing of workshops for example, by both in-patients and out-patients which would be more economic and convenient, particularly in areas of low population density.

A relevant point of discussion here is the size of hospital most appropriate for the care of the mentally disordered which is a very controversial issue at present. At the moment psychiatric hospitals tend to be large, and in-patient populations of 1500–2000 are not uncommon. There are cogent arguments for reducing the size of mental hospitals on the grounds that these are at present so large that they are necessarily impersonal in their approach. This means that patients cannot be allowed freedom to develop independence at their own pace nor can they have the basic human liberties which are the right of any normal person. Care becomes institution-oriented rather than patient-oriented, and patients suffer as a result. Children become socially retarded, especially with regard to speech, and adults experience personality deterioration. There is now substantial experimental evidence to support this thesis. [8, 9]

Because of purely administrative variables, such as the fact that pay for top nursing, medical, and administrative staff increases with the number of patients they control, there are pressures to keep hospitals large in size which have nothing to do with the possible benefit or otherwise to the patient. However, there are some arguments for retaining large hospitals, based on patient needs, and staff well-being which do carry some weight. A large population of patients is required to justify the expense of specialized ancillary services, such as physiotherapy, dental treatment, chiropody, speech therapy, etc.; large hospital populations facilitate research into treatment and training methods; staff function better with stimulation from colleagues, and this is possible only if patient numbers are large; large hospitals, and the consequent possibility of working in or of running a large department, attract more ambitious and go-ahead staff. The validity of some of these points may be debatable but they would in any case be answered if hospital and community services were run together. The large patient population would still be available, together with the variety of services and staff, but this population would include both residential-based and home-based patients, and therefore the size of the residential units could be reduced.

We have argued that the present tripartite administration with the strict division of responsibility between local authority, G.P.s, and hospitals is quite anachronistic in the context of the current treatments and patterns of care which are or should be available for the mentally disordered. In fact, the existing administrative barriers militate against the development of the kind of services we now realize that these patients require. In Chapter 10 we shall discuss experiments to co-ordinate the services within the existing framework and how successful these have been. We shall also suggest how much better co-ordination could be if the present administrative divisions were abolished.

CHAPTER 6

Reform of Local and Central Government in Relation to the National Health Service Reform

ANYONE concerned for reform in local or central government must be aware of the increasing tendency for control to pass to the bureaucratic machine. This is the essence of the "democratic dilemma" and to postulate changes in structure without allowing for, and analysing, this trend would be to abdicate from possibly the most fundamental issue in any reform of government.

Reform of Parliament and reform of local government cannot be thought of independently. To succeed they need to be closely integrated. Because of the isolation imposed by their structure in the past, both have suffered, not only in their administrative competence but also in their progressive dissociation from individual participation and involvement. Reorganization must endeavour to satisfy both the criterion of competence and of democratic participation, for it is doubtful in the long term whether it is possible to achieve an efficient administration if it is divorced from and insensitive to the aspirations and grievances of the individual.

At present we have only to contend with frustration as manifested in back-bench discontent, regional protest voting, and the growth of consumer movements. These are positive reactions which, if correctly harnessed, could provide a productive and creative force. The danger is that the frustrations will fester and turn sour, developing into a negative destructive drive which will either result in an increasing tendency to opt out of the democratic process, or will harden into a posture of contempt for the democratic machine.

It is worth noting in this context the deep sense of frustration felt by those working in the health service. The increasing criticism, particularly inside the N.H.S., is indicative of an administrative breakdown. In this service which, more than any other, should reflect consumer wishes, there is a widening gap between the administrators and consumers. The growth of patients' associations is a manifestation of the inadequate machinery for any form of client control or protest. Yet any change in the administrative structure of the N.H.S. must be seen against the wider background of administrative reform. With the recommendations for local government reform for Wales already published, and the Royal Commission for Scotland and England soon to report, we must seriously consider how the N.H.S. can be brought into a closer relationship with the local authorities. Reform of parliamentary procedure is also very relevant to this discussion.

The challenge is to build into any new structure the outlet for participation in decision making yet, at the same time, streamlining and centralizing the procedure. No one expects, despite the recent controversy, to be able to reform Parliament in the direction of restoring the individual voting freedom that characterized Parliament a century ago. The party machine and its embrace will now stay, and it is at least arguable that its general effect has been beneficial. Reform must take the path of allowing the individual member an outlet for his frustrations and it is against this background that the movement towards more select committees of the House of Commons should be judged a significant advance. It is reasonable to hope that a select committee on social welfare will be established and through such a committee it should be possible for the member not only to probe and influence, but also to initiate research and anticipate legislation. The most depressing experience for any intelligent mind is to be confined to "conversational research" dealing exclusively in second-hand opinions and thoughts. This is the really stultifying factor that faces the present-day M.P. Increasingly he has been deprived of the right to vote independently and has failed to build up, as a counter-balancing force, the machinery to wield a formative influence on the legislative programme prior to its presentation. This role, which could have been Parliament's, has instead been confined almost exclusively to royal commissions and special committees. As a result the conscientious M.P. has turned, perhaps in desperation, into the important but limited role of a universal ombudsman to constituents to an extent that is rapidly becoming an absurdity. At the same time, since Ministers are expected to answer all letters from M.P.s without any selection or discrimination being used, not surprisingly their burden increases every year. The disastrous consequence of this is to reduce the flow of real indicative thinking or contingency planning emerging from all levels of Parliament. It is, in fact, impossible for an M.P. to write to the information office of a department requesting solely factual information without his inquiry being channelled through a Minister and eliciting a 4-week delay. Even the parliamentary question is largely a public relations exercise with very little real information being unearthed.

By bowing to the traditional trappings and outward manifestations of a democratic process, we have actively inhibited the Member or Minister from serving as an effective check on the bureaucratic machine. The democratic process is in many cases a total illusion, spread so thin that it can never penetrate, superficially all-embracing, and yet so lacking any depth that its forays on behalf of the individual are repeatedly repulsed by the administrative machine. Ministers, M.P.s, councillors, all have become bogged down by the complexity of modern living to the extent that their ability to act and protect the individual is threatened. Tacit recognition of this is given in the appointment of the Parliamentary Commissioner, although as yet his function is so circumscribed that inevitably his impact will be limited. It is regrettable that the Minister of Health resisted very considerable parliamentary pressure to extend the scope of the

Parliamentary Commissioner to investigate the health service. [1] It may be that this will soon be done but there is also a case for considering the establishment of a special parliamentary Health Commissioner with a specific expertise in this admittedly very complicated field for objective assessment. Many M.P.s feel that in the health service there are many constituents' complaints that appear to warrant full investigation. The recent public disquiet following the publication of the book *Sans Everything* [2] revealed a totally inadequate procedure for ensuring an objective inquiry. It is beyond dispute that if a "health ombudsman" already existed there would have been no allegations of bias or fears about the confidentiality of the evidence to the inquiry that was set up. The Council on Tribunals in their 1966 report also state their anxiety about the present arrangements for handing complaints before the medical service committees of the executive councils.

Members of Parliament should be given the opportunity to participate in outside inquiries and advisory bodies. There is also no valid reason for excluding members of the governing party from greater participation inside the Ministries in which they have particular interest or expertise. Their position need not be formalized beyond being bound by the Official Secrets Act—they would not need to have extra salaries and their commitment to the Government need extend no further than the policy stemming from the particular Ministry. The existence of the office of parliamentary private secretary could be the precedent, although this is rarely accompanied by any real role within the department. At the moment we perpetuate the absurd conspiracy of silence, fostered by the Civil Service, and keep from M.P.s documents to which the most junior civil servant has open access. Nothing is more dangerous than ill-informed criticism, and in consequence the gap between the Government and their supporters in Parliament can become ridiculously wide. It is becoming obvious that this situation will not be readily tolerated by the younger intake. Parliament is starting, albeit slowly, to reform itself and although the outcome will only emerge piecemeal, it seems likely that the result will be to inhance the influence and penetration of its Members and Ministers.

Since we write before the Royal Commission on Local Government Reform has published its recommendations, it is necessary to outline possible solutions for local government reform, and then to discuss its integration with the health and welfare services. Reform of local government is certain to meet a similar resistance to that which has met all attempts at parliamentary reform. The crucial reform that is now being contemplated is whether to settle for first-tier regional government. If the evidence of the civil servants from the different Ministries is any guide (although one hopes it is not), we are likely to be landed with a miserable compromise that has neither the benefits of regionalism nor of truly local government. The proposed first-tier structure of city regions of between 30–40 units will simply ensure the perpetuation of the isolation of local government, both from Whitehall and from the individual. It will offer only one real advance, and that is to reduce the number of overall units of local government. One obvious attraction, which will not have escaped establishment thinking, is that it has possibly the greatest prospect of winning wide acceptance. The apparent unanimity of the Civil Service evidence to the Commission is itself suspicious. However, it is interesting to record that in the debate in Parliament on local government reform, feeling was almost wholly in favour of a large regional first-tier structure. [3]

One great weakness in our present system of local government arises because it is a hybrid with no structural links with the central government, or easy access to government decision making. It follows from this that local government has never played an integral part in any national policies and this has often been found to be an impediment to any central planning. The proposals for regional government are an attempt to resolve this deficiency, provide a structural link, and ensure that many of the functions of local authorities would be exercised over larger areas. Yet a fundamental requirement for any regional policy is a small number of units with 15 as a maximum, and 12 a better target figure. A system where there are 40–50 units (for the proposed number of 30–40 will undoubtedly increase as a result of local pressure) will make it impossible to achieve the close structural link between central government and the regions. Regionalism stands or falls on the transfer of many government department functions, leaving only major policy decision making and overall planning to be centred in Whitehall. An elected regional council should ideally have a direct working relationship with government departments in the region, although the regional departments will remain answerable to the Minister and Parliament. The leader of the region must retain the vital right of direct access to the Minister, which the chairmen of the present Regional Economic Planning Councils already possess. All the main government departments in the regions would work with paid elected regional chairmen appointed by the regional council from their number, who would have to be subject to the Official Secrets Act in a similar manner to Ministers. Similarly, their relationship with the regional body and regional government departments would mirror the present relationship of a Minister to his department and M.P.s. It would not be necessary to appoint a separate regional Minister serving in Parliament since this would destroy the essential national decision making process of Parliament and disrupt departmental responsibility.

The growth of nationalism and regional feeling can be seen as an underlying influence in the 1966 Carmarthen and 1967 Hamilton by-elections and this is unlikely to represent a merely transient frustration. It is therefore urgent that the Government should quickly provide the necessary regional machinery to channel these feelings so that they develop within a coherent framework. Nationalism or regionalism without such an outlet can easily become a dangerous emotional force, manifesting itself in a manner that can only destroy any rational planning of regional and local government. The special relationship that exists for Wales and Scotland will obviously remain, but there is no case for duplicating this region by region. Instead the necessary parliamentary links should be maintained by regional select committees. Since the Lords is to be reformed it is worth deliberately seeking to represent the regions, and the formation of select committees with members from both Houses is a possibility which could be a significant advance in central representation of regional feeling.

The regional councils would consist of elected part-time members paid for attendance, and coming together for something like a week every quarter. The question as to whether they should be directly elected members or delegates from the second-tier authority is arguable. The advantage of the latter alternative is that it would avoid elections for completely new areas and ensure that there would always be the closest liaison between the local and regional tiers of government. For regionalism does not mean the end of local government but merely the rationalization of some of its functions. At the same time some directly elected councillors would ensure that younger people were given the opportunity which they might not otherwise get, since nominated members would tend to be long-serving members of the local authority. A mixed composition might therefore be the best solution.

The second-tier authority would be based on the concept of the city region, but could show considerable variation in size between urban and rural areas, and their representation on the regional body would reflect population, although it would be hoped that they would not number more than 100. It would not be necessary therefore to impose unified standards of population and size and, in deciding boundaries, the main factor would be to determine the most efficient administrative unit. The functions of the second-tier authority would, primarily, be concerned with acting as the individual's link with the decision making process and, where local authorities already serve this purpose, their powers would be maintained and strengthened. The new unit of local government would be larger than the present ones, but deal with many of the same functions. In addition, their members would serve on local area health boards, local educational executives, and would retain supervisory powers over housing allocation and maintenance. The local unit would have its own members in the regional council but instead of dealing with Whitehall, as at present, would liaise direct with the regional government departments who would be in a position to take decisions at the regional level. Local councillors, instead of involving themselves so deeply in detailed decisions, would concentrate on broad managerial decisions, would serve increasingly as the representatives of the consumer, and would exert a degree of client watchfulness and control that has been lacking in many sectors of local administration.

This structure is deliberately designed to link the local councillor with the regional council, hoping in this way to off-set the inevitable down-grading of the second-tier authority and offer the possibility to councillors of achieving the stature of regional councillors. This reform would allow decentralization, yet retain a marked degree of overall control spreading right down to the smallest local unit. The functional division between regional and local government would be determined by present government departments. The regional council's main responsibilities would be for the strategic planning of education, housing, land use, industrial location, and health and welfare. The present regional departments of government such as Ministry of Labour, Board of Trade, Department of Economic Affairs, and Technology, would be preserved and a working relationship established between them and the regional council. An essential implication, of course, is the rationalization of boundaries for the numerous existing regional bodies, so that, as far as possible, all would have boundaries coterminous with the first-tier regional councils.

There is also a need for a community or neighbourhood council that would have no executive function but could act as the voice of the community within the local unit. It would concern itself particularly with the practical functioning of the community services and have the right to be consulted on all planning decisions at an early stage, so that the community interest could be heard before irrevocable decisions had been made. This would not be a third-tier of local government, but represent in urban areas the equivalent to the present ward and inject into that lifeless political unit the community responsibility that it wholly lacks at present. In rural areas it would replace the parish council. Whether a community council would be elected or appointed could be left open. Initially it might be more likely to succeed (especially in some cities where no traditional community spirit exists) if political ward parties and other organizations active in the neighbourhood nominated members. Once the initial apathy was overcome, elections would almost certainly follow. Any reform of local government that does not allow for individual identification at the community level will only perpetuate the existing barriers. What is needed is a structure that fosters individual participation by a series of overlapping, but functionally distinct, units of government.

It is, of course, perfectly possible that the Royal Commission will not recommend such a regional structure and may, in fact, recommend 30–40 city regions. This would pose a number of urgent questions: in the field of health planning, could one abolish altogether the regional hospital boards and fuse their role with that of the hospital management committees (H.M.C.s) and form 30–40 area health boards (A.H.B.s)? This would mean a one-tier health authority. A forceful argument against this would be that in health, which must be peculiarly sensitive to community feelings, such a large authority would lose the intimacy and local flavour that it is vital for the area health board to retain. For this reason we would prefer approximately 90–100 A.H.B.s for an A.H.B. can be too large. Faced with 30–40 first-tier regions one would have to examine the size of the second-tier authorities, possibly using combinations of authorities where they are very small to form A.H.B.s, and leaving the first-tier city regions to replace the present regional hospital boards. This would clearly be a less satisfactory solution than that which would operate if the Royal Commission did recommend the larger regions as a first-tier authority, and we are taking this reform as the basis for our detailed health proposals.

The regional concept of planning already exists in hospital administration and it has played an important role in rationalizing resources, but the need is to link the existing systems with any local government reform so as to allow an integrated administrative structure for the health and welfare services. Central government should fuse the Ministries of Social Security, Health and the Children's Department of the Home Office into one Ministry of Social Affairs with a Secretary of State at its head with Ministers of State for Health, Social Welfare and Social Security. At a regional level, the combined Ministry would have a direct relationship with the Regional Health Board (R.H.B.), formed from elected members of the regional council with a proportion of co-opted members. At its head would be a paid chairman who would draw a financial honorarium to cover the time and expense of his duties. This would replace the present regional hospital board and the functions of the R.H.B. would embrace a unified health service comprising hospitals, G.P.s, and the present health and welfare services of local authorities. A.H.B.s would be established to coincide with the boundaries assigned to the second-tier local authority and their function would be to administer the local aspects of the unified services. Their members would come predominantly from the local councillors, elected to the second-tier authority that the A.H.B. served. A reasonable proportion of co-opted members with specialist knowledge would also serve on the A.H.B.s which would absorb present H.M.C. functions. These reforms, ridding the health service of its present tripartite structure, would continue the regional element in health planning which has already been shown to be necessary, would at last bring the health services within the structure of local government, and would ensure more democratic control and answerability to the consumer.

An important part of any reform must be to ensure that the community feels that it has a real stake in its local services including the local hospital. This element of local pride and concern for what is in the midst of the community was one good aspect of the system prior to the introduction of the N.H.S. which has, to some extent, been lost. The house committees for local hospitals represent an effort to retain this feeling of identification and participation, and though invested with no executive powers, they do have the right to make regular visits to the hospital and inspect standards and make recommendations to the H.M.C.s. A recent report on hospitals has recommended the abolition of house committees[4] and in certain areas this has already happened. It is an extraordinary comment on the Minister of Health's role that he does not feel able to make any judgement on this issue, and is content to leave the decision to the H.M.C. If participation in the health service is not to cease this trend must be watched very carefully. It can be argued that a League of Friends could undertake many of the functions of the house committees and this is undoubtedly true. In those cases, where it is felt desirable to close the house committees, it would seem reasonable to give the committee of the League of Friends the same rights of access as is given to the house committees.

There is obviously room for experiment, but real participation needs to carry some measure of responsibility, while it is right that participation at this level should not carry executive powers. With the larger areas that would be covered by the A.H.B.s the local hospitals, perhaps separated by a distance of 25 miles in some places, will inevitably form a local administrative centre and in these cases there must be a sensitive structure for a responsible element of local participation. It may be that if neighbourhood councils were formed, some of their members would serve on such house committees. The administrator will, quite correctly, increasingly demand the right to make managerial decisions and not be hamstrung by endless committees; but if this trend is to be allowed to continue, then it is important to build into the system adequate mechanisms for consumer participation and access. In a world of increasingly rapid change, which necessitates machinery for quick decisions, we need to evolve side by side a flexible approach which recognizes that the rights of access and consultation are powerful democratic tools and, in many respects, are every bit as effective in representing consumer interests as the tedious involvement in every-day management decisions.

We have rejected from the outset any proposal to transfer the hospital and G.P. services direct to local government. In principle, the initial proposals by Ernest Brown in 1943 were probably the nearest one could have approached to any such arrangement, but it was no accident that they were withdrawn then, and there is no evidence that the opposition now would be any the less. Whatever personal views we might hold on this issue, we are convinced that the pressure, predominantly led by the medical profession, would still be too strong to permit the integration of the service directly under the control of the reorganized local government authority. We have therefore deliberately excluded discussing any such proposition purely on the grounds of its impracticality. There will always be some revolutionary theorists who will condemn such an attitude, but before doing so it would be wise for them to reflect on the situation that faced Kenneth Robinson on taking office in 1964, and how, in the subsequent negotiations with 18,000 resignations held by the B.M.A., the medical profession were able to exert pressure that no politician or political party could apparently ignore. The opportunity for the revolutionary solution was in effect lost in 1946. We are left only with the possibility of attempting an evolutionary solution. This is not necessarily regrettable, for the whole history of the health service in this country has been an evolving one. Attitudes have often proved a far greater limitation to progress than any structure and it could well be argued that even if, in 1946, a unified structure had been imposed, the movement towards community care and responsibility would have taken just as long, and would only have taken advantage of the structural integration comparatively recently.

Our proposals for an A.H.B. are also an attempt to meet some of the major objections to the creation of *ad hoc* health authorities on a local basis mirroring the present regional hospital boards. The Guillebaud Report rejected the *ad hoc* health authority in the following important paragraph:

> Even apart from practical considerations, such as the question of the composition of such all-purpose authorities, we consider this suggestion unacceptable because it would remove from the local health authorities their important domiciliary health services and would create a division between different types of public health work at least as unfortunate as the present divisions within the National Health Service. It would, moreover, drive a wedge between the home health services now provided by local health authorities under Part III of the National Health Service Act and the welfare services provided by local authorities under Part III of the National Assistance Act—a division which would, in our view, be calamitous.

The A.H.B.s, we suggest, are designed to meet these objections and differ significantly from the outline proposals contained in the Porritt Report. This report recommended that the health services of the country should be planned over areas specifically designed to meet the needs of the community they serve, and envisaged new boundaries solely to meet the demands of community medical care; and they also proposed that the teaching hospital should continue, as at present in England and Wales, to be administered by separate boards of governors with direct access to the Minister.

Our proposals, however, do attempt to avoid the problem of driving a wedge between the home health services and the welfare services. Increasingly local authorities have themselves felt it necessary to integrate these two functions and have often fused the two departments into a unified health and welfare department. It would therefore be against the trend of integration to propose a division of such functions, particularly between two different bodies. We have therefore felt, in contradistinction to Porritt, that it is right that local authority welfare functions under the 1948 National Assistance Act for residential accommodation for old people, for substantially and permanently handicapped persons or for the homeless, should be transferred to the A.H.B. It will be argued that not only will this take away from local authorities one of their major functions, and emasculate their power and consequently their ability to attract good quality councillors, but that it will mean that an even larger financial burden will be put on the Exchequer.

We feel very strongly, in fact, that a single financial system covering the hospital and the local health services alike is essential. It is worth noting that there is already tacit recognition of the fact that the local authorities cannot bear the cost of the health and welfare services on their own, in that it is financed only in part by the rates. Against the background of substantial rate relief from central government, and mounting hostility to rising rates, it seems that the cost of an integrated service would have to be borne by the Exchequer, certainly until substantial reform had taken place involving the present rating system. It would similarly be very difficult to see Parliament giving to any local authority very substantial grants to run a service over which they had little or no control; and to raise the money solely by local taxation would be a considerable, though not impossible, undertaking.

The question of reducing the power, influence, and effectiveness of the local authority is, we consider, a major objection and to meet this we propose a number of radical departures from most schemes for integration. We reject the fact that the boundaries of the A.H.B. should be specifically determined by the need of community medical care. We believe that most important of all should be the many considerations, not by any means solely medical, which go to form a community area. Particularly in welfare this involves the very factors which will guide the Royal Commission in their delineation of any second-tier authority, and we believe that the balance of advantage to the health services as a whole strongly favours, in all but perhaps exceptional circumstances deriving from geography, boundaries for the A.H.B.s conforming to the boundaries of the second-tier local authority areas. It is, for instance, already the case that the commission will be determining these areas with the local authority health and welfare services very much in mind. With the introduction of the concept of the district general hospital, the community will increasingly have in its midst hospitals designed to give a comprehensive community service: to establish separate areas will lead only to a further divorce of the hospital services from the community they serve. We are, anyhow, extremely sceptical about the possibility of defining a boundary solely for health, especially when this would have to be done at a time when all thinking on medical care is extremely fluid, and experimentation and controversy are so common. There are many disadvantages stemming from the present system where the regional hospital boards frequently cross over local authority boundaries.

This leads on to an important criticism of the present structure of both the hospital and G.P. service, in that their accountability is totally confined at local and regional level to appointed boards. The demand for some degree of democratic representation, if not control, has been persistent and, we believe, justified. We therefore propose that the R.H.B. and A.H.B. should retain a majority of members nominated from the democratically elected first and second-tiers of local government. As most people know who have served on such committees with a mixed composition, this would not in any way lessen the essential and important role of the appointed members, but it would ensure that what would in effect be the health committee of the local authority would be intimately involved, as of right, in the management of the integrated health service. Instead of the present situation, where no one in the community feels that he has either any knowledge of why, or say in how, someone is appointed, there would be a clear-cut identification of the local authority, and hence the elector, with the running of the N.H.S.

Parliament, through the Secretary of State for Social Affairs, would have an overall influence and retain financial control. The Minister would be able to ensure minimum standards of provision, and this is particularly necessary in the field of the present health and welfare services where some local authorities ignore ministerial circulars, and either make inadequate or no provision for services which more enlightened authorities consider essential. At the same time, the Ministry would deliberately de-volve to the R.H.B.s some of its powers and decision making, and R.H.B.s would continue to experiment and innovate within their region. The Ministry should adopt a new and more positive role of pioneering methods and attempting a radical delineation of minimum standards with the backing of mandatory legislation. The inequalities of provision and care that exist at present must be eradicated and this would be a major benefit to accrue from the introduction of a truly unified N.H.S.

CHAPTER 7

The Organization of a Unified National Health Service

WE HAVE discussed in earlier chapters what we consider to be the major disadvantages of the present tripartite structure of the health service, which is that by operating through three adminis- trative bodies, each with limited and defined sectors of activity, solutions are pursued which may be administratively convenient and apparently efficient from the view-point of each of the separate branches, but which frequently are not advantageous to the functioning of the health service overall. Hence the pre- disposition to fragmentation rather than co-ordination, in what should be complementary services. The widely differing struc- tures and backgrounds of these three administrative bodies likewise hinders unity. The administrative heads of the three sections at a local level, the medical officer of health, the clerk to the executive council and the hospital group secretary are not in any sense equivalent to each other, either in terms of status or in the extent of their executive responsibilities. In consequence, it becomes exceedingly difficult to liaise over a problem for which all three sections have some responsibility.

There are two basic alternatives in contemplating a reorganized service. One is to attempt to integrate the existing structures and the other is to adopt a totally new unified structure. The former solution would involve grouping the three present structures under one commmittee or board with a subcommittee representing each of the three sections, which would liaise and co-ordinate on a local basis. The Porritt Committee appeared inclined to this scheme, although it is easy to misinterpret their intentions.

This solution, however, assumes that there is already appropriate management within the separate branches and that co-ordination can be achieved by the amalgamation of management bodies. We reject this assumption entirely.

In the first place there is neither equality of management between the three branches nor equivalence in their geographical boundaries of operation. In addition, in some sections there is too much rule by committee, in others too much autocracy, and in others insufficient democratic representation of the consumer. Furthermore, the existence of three separate but overlapping services does not allow for the most efficient use of limited resources. Finally, enough has been learnt since 1948 about the management of large organizations and the economies of large-scale undertakings to demand a complete reappraisal and a more radical approach to the design of an integrated health service. We therefore would prefer to organize the health service on a geographical basis, under one management structure.

One of the problems at present encountered is the proliferation of boundaries for management both within the N.H.S. and between it and other services which are closely related to health. A major guiding point in reorganization should therefore be to co-ordinate boundaries for health with boundaries which exist for other economic, social, and welfare agencies. This is the prime reason why we consider that the establishment of *ad hoc* areas for health would be quite unacceptable. For the planning of an effective service on a geographical basis, it is obviously essential for the planning body to have basic information on, for example, population densities and trends, transport facilities within the area, and the planned expansion of any new service which is likely to effect the need for health provision. To liaise effectively with other social services, e.g. education, it is at least preferable that all services function within the same geographical boundaries. Furthermore, *ad hoc* areas for health would divorce the health services entirely from democratic control or influence, except at national level.

Since local government reform is imminent, it would seem the most rational course, as we have argued previously, is to tie the boundaries for health into the reorganized local government structure. The new structure for local government will form the basis for the organization of the other related services and presumably also for the collection of basic statistics. Linking health with local government will also provide a means whereby the consumer, or his elected representatives, can exert an influence on the health services.

It seems likely that the new structure of local government will be a two-tier system although it is difficult to argue in advance of the Royal Commission Report what size the units will be or what will be the separate functions of the two tiers. In the previous chapter we argued in favour of 12–15 regions as a first tier. The arguments in favour of organizing the health service on a regional basis, with population units of several millions, are primarily organizational. That is, many of the essential managerial functions of a health service can be carried out more effectively with units of this scale, partly because of the economies possible in a large undertaking, but also because of the limited supply of top-grade management or professional skills. We may well have sufficient high-grade staff to operate 10 or 15 regional health boards (R.H.B.s), but it is unlikely that we could get the same managerial efficiency for 90 or 100. In addition there are many aspects of health which require a very large catchment area for their operation, either because they are concerned with relatively rare conditions, e.g. specialist cardiac surgery or because of the limited number of trained professional staff available, e.g. steroid chemistry. Therefore if R.H.B.s were too small in size, it would not be possible to provide a full-range service and it is difficult to ensure the proper development of services which have to be shared between areas.

Smaller units, corresponding to the second tier of the reformed local government structure, would form the basis for the area health boards (A.H.B.s). The A.H.B. would act as the unit for organizing the basic local health services, hospitals, G.P.s, and community services, but on an integrated pattern. Again it is not possible to predict in advance of the Royal Commission Report what size these will be, but they are unlikely to be any smaller than the London boroughs (at present approximately 200,000) and will probably be considerably larger. At this size, A.H.B.s would be large enough to be self-sufficient in the basic services, but small enough to allow for some element of local involvement by the community which we feel is so vital. Once again the correspondence of health boundaries with boundaries for other services, run by local government, particularly housing and education, would make it possible for better liaison between services and for the sharing of facilities where this is appropriate.

In brief, the new structure we propose would be as follows. At national level, health would be the responsibility of a Secretary of State for Health, under a new combined Ministry for Health and Social Services (see Chapter 6). Under the Minister and directly responsible to him would be the R.H.B.s, which operate all the health services, including training programmes and teaching hospitals within their catchment area. Each region would be divided into A.H.B.s, coterminous with local government areas. At the more local level, each A.H.B. would comprise eventually general hospitals, whose catchment areas would form the basis for the organization of general medical and community services.

Within any large organization quite different kinds of decisions have to be taken at different levels. In relation to the health service, for example, at the national level questions concerning staff should be focused on topics such as recruitment methods, policy for training staff and deployment, while at the local level questions concerning staff would concentrate on issues such as effective team collaboration, satisfactory sharing of premises, and adequate duty rosters. In order that sound decisions are taken at each level, it is essential that the appropriate information be available and that people with appropriate skills are empowered to take decisions. With these points in mind we will now discuss the role and function of each management tier of the health service as we envisage it.

The Ministry

Under the system we have outlined, the Ministry would be responsible for the overall planning of all aspects of the Service, and the determination of major policy issues affecting staffing, buildings, and equipment. In order to determine community needs and the staff and resources required, much more use should be made of research studies than is usual at present. Major policy decisions should be based on systematic work and not on the expression of mere opinion, however eminent may be the people who are called upon for particular advisory committees. The provision of such research should be the responsibility of the Ministry, which would sponsor projects, to be carried out in conjunction with the R.H.B.s. Research skills are scarce and the money for complex organizational research is restricted, and therefore it would be impossible to provide each region with its own comprehensive research organization. With co-operation between the Ministry and the regions, however, the results of studies in one or two areas could be used as the basis for national policy.

On the basis of such studies the Ministry would decide the minimum criterion necessary for such things as the operation of maternity services, training centres, or mobile X-ray units. It would also be the function of the Ministry to ensure that these minimum requirements were fulfilled. At present local or regional variations in services exist which cannot be rationally explained. One would like to see the Ministry taking positive steps to promote good standards and pioneer new methods. At present the Ministry merely urges various lines of action and rarely, if at all, insists on particular measures. Unrestricted visiting for children's wards, the provision of lockers for the private possessions of the chronic mentally ill, units for the care of adolescent psychiatric patients, remain largely an unfulfilled dream, despite numerous Ministry circulars. These facts surely indicate the need for firm guidance and an equally firm insistence that things are done and not silently obstructed.

One effective method for raising standards and enforcing them would be the establishment of Ministry liaison officers who would visit regions and ensure that Ministry requirements were being met. If there was under-provision in some areas of, for example, health visitors, nursery nurses, or beds for the young chronic sick, the regional board and the liaison officer would discuss these issues and decide in what ways matters could be remedied. Areas which are particularly poor in provision would be designated priority areas, similar to the education priority areas indicated in the Plowden Report, [1] where special resources and energies need to be concentrated.

The Ministry would also be responsible for seeing that provision was made for the education of staff of different grades and specialities and for determining the content of training. This would allow the Ministry to play a very important part in defining the role of different types of staff, so that new roles could be evolved as the needs of the community changed.

The Regional Health Boards

Since each region would differ somewhat in population density and distribution and in particular needs, the main function of the R.H.B. would be to decide how best to apply Ministry policy in each particular region. The R.H.B. would have available through the regional government departments the information on demography, transport, economic development, and housing policies, necessary to plan health services in any area. Thus the siting of services would be decided at regional level, but within the framework of the scales of provision determined at Ministry level.

It is perhaps unfortunate that the term "Regional Health Board" has to be used—although it is the most appropriate—as it lends itself to confusion with the present Regional *Hospital* Boards. In theory these boards are "responsible for the planning and development of the hospital and specialist services, for all capital works, for the provision of special services such as blood transfusion and for the appointment of senior medical staff"

(*M.H. Handbook*). In practice these responsibilities have been shaped, during the formative years, from 1948, by secretaries recruited from either local government or the overseas civil service, and the boards have tended to become much too involved in day-to-day administration and bureaucratic procedures. By exercising particularly tight financial control over the hospital management committees (H.M.C.s), in their regions they have allowed themselves to fall into the trap of being unable to concentrate on the major issues. Whilst this feeling rarely appears in print, evidence was presented to the Farquharson-Lang Committee that "Regional Boards . . . . had become too immersed in the more detailed management functions belonging to Boards of Management" (the Scottish equivalent to hospital management committees). This criticism was recognized in the committee's recommendation that the respective responsibilities should be clarified, and the committee chairman's reported view that boards should not concern themselves with the details of policy execution.

The definition of responsibilities for the proposed R.H.B., and its relationship with the A.H.B.s therefore needs careful attention. There will be an inevitable interaction between the board's major function of setting objectives, and that of checking progress in order to achieve the highest standards of care through a unified service. Generally one would like to see the boards applying national policy and principles in respect of the medical services, embracing both provision of staff and major capital programmes, whilst the area boards would carry out the detailed reviews. The regional board, acting as a sub-body of the regional council, is ideally placed to see the region as a whole, to survey all services, to highlight defects and then to remedy them. Its existence offers an opportunity to plan major increases in urban populations in harmony with such factors as health, welfare, education, and water resources. In the past the involvement of local authorities has been lacking or tardy, while the provision of hospital services in new towns hardly bears examination as part of the chronological development of such towns.

Besides the overall planning and operation of health services, the establishment of new buildings and the control of expenditure, R.H.B.s would have much to offer on strictly practical and economic grounds. Many of the specialist service units or industrial functions of the N.H.S., such as architecture, heating and ventilation engineering, and data processing could be more efficiently provided at regional level, rather than allowing each A.H.B. to develop their own services independently. The Oxford Regional Hospital Board is at present planning to concentrate what are called the "industrial" functions of the hospital service into five "area industrial zones". [2] Each of these will include a laundry, a sterile goods preparation unit, a pharmaceutical manufacturing unit, a pathology processing unit, and facilities for central stores, food preparation, and storage. Each "industrial zone" will be serviced by its own transport department and run by its own administrative unit. These are all functions which now tend to be operated by H.M.C. for its own hospitals, but can be provided more efficiently if operated on a larger scale and with specialized management. Under the reorganized structure we propose, these utilities would be provided by the region for groups of A.H.B.s and the industrial units would service, not only hospitals, but also the other health departments which need the same facilities, e.g. nurseries, meals on wheels, training centres, etc. Under such a system the contracts arranged centrally now by the Ministries of Health and Public Works will also need to be adapted and integrated. The keynote in the provision of such arrangements must be service and not uniformity. Central buying at present often leads to the provision of inferior goods at cut prices. Regional organization must offer proven advantages and a first-class service.

R.H.B.s would also be involved in the recruitment, training and provision of staff. Together with the Ministry liaison officer, each board would decide on the staffing policy appropriate in that region, in order to fulfil Ministry requirements and ensure that the training facilities were available to meet the staffing ratios laid down in Ministry policy. Teaching hospitals would be incorporated into the regional structure, but additional facilities for the training of managerial and other staff would also be necessary. Some might be provided at national level, of course, but this would be a decision reached by discussion between the Ministry and the regions.

For the recruitment of staff the principle would be that decisions should be taken at a high enough level to allow skill in selecting personnel and at a low enough level to allow local participation in the selection. The regional boards would therefore of necessity be involved in the appointment of relatively rare, highly specialized staff, but for most other members of staff, such as nurses, appointment at a local level would be more appropriate and this practice exists in the present structure.

The Area Health Board

The A.H.B. would be responsible for the day-to-day management and integration of in-patients and community services within its own area. The A.H.B. would work jointly with the region to ensure the adequacy of services within the area and consult with the region on any contingency planning that might be necessary. An A.H.B. with a teaching hospital within its catchment area would have the additional responsibility of effecting liaison with the university concerned, assuming that the teaching hospital will act in the future, not only as a training and research establishment but also as one of the district general hospitals. In Scotland this artificial separation between teaching and general hospitals does not exist and there is no evidence that the medical schools have suffered. Rather it appears that there is far greater community identification and responsibility which cannot but be reflected in the attitude of the newly-trained doctor.

At A.H.B. level there would also be opportunity to co-ordinate the health services with other services organized by local government and there would need to be some formal structure for liaison between the A.H.B. and the other services, such as education and housing. At the field level this liaison might operate through the use of joint premises where this was appropriate, but this kind of decision would be taken as a result of A.H.B. consultation with the local government departments.

Because of its direct link with local government, perhaps the most important function of the A.H.B. would be to represent the "consumer" by careful attention to consultation and the fostering of local participation. We have mentioned already the composition of the A.H.B. These would be drawn partly from the elected local government councillors and the rest would be appointed members, who would be mainly professional representatives, such as doctors, nurses, and medical social workers. It would be through this committee that consumer interest would be safeguarded. We suggest that there should be facilities at the level of each local unit (local hospital, health centre or community care unit) for the reception of complaints and suggestions, and that this should be encouraged by the local unit administrators. At A.H.B. level there should also be machinery for ensuring that complaints have been adequately dealt with. The administrator of each field unit should be obliged to forward to the A.H.B. a statement of all complaints and suggestions made to him and the action taken in response. Any individual could refer complaints to the A.H.B. direct and if he was not satisfied with the action taken he could always have recourse through his Member of Parliament to the proposed Health Commissioner.

CHAPTER 8

The Management and Administration of the Area Health Board

It is sometimes suggested as a reason for integrating the health services completely under local government that this would ensure a better administrative arrangement involving less duplication. The health and welfare administrative section would merely be enlarged and legal and financial issues would become the responsibility of the appropriate local government departments. Apart from the political arguments against this arrangement to which we have already referred and which, in our judgement, makes this impractical, there are quite separate administrative issues. Since 1946 health administration has become a speciality in its own right although it is true that this has probably been too hospital oriented. Within the hospital service and the local executive council, a structure for health administration has been built up which is quite different to that obtaining for local government, and which has developed its own specialized legal and financial skills. These could be utilized in the structure we propose. The Area Health Board (A.H.B.) would involve a large administrative area, would work on a sizeable budget and would represent, by itself, a viable administrative unit.

We have argued in an earlier chapter that a unified service will have to have only one source of finance and that this should come centrally from the Exchequer. It may be that with the advent of regionalism some form of local income tax may be introduced and this could be used to finance in part the regional health service. Meanwhile, if the Minister is to have power to enforce minimum standards of provision and the second-tier authority is to lose direct control of its existing health and welfare functions, it is not reasonable to expect the rates to continue to carry the cost of these services, although, as we have already stated, these are heavily subsidized by grants from central government even at present. It would be preferable, we suggest, to retain and enlarge the scope of the existing central N.H.S. finance.

As we have indicated in a previous chapter, the Regional Health Board (R.H.B.) would be responsible for overall planning and would therefore ultimately be responsible for determining annual budgets in consultation with the A.H.B.s. However, the R.H.B. should allow the A.H.B. considerable freedom for day-to-day management, so that the A.H.B. would have more managerial autonomy within its budget than exists for the present Hospital Management Committee (H.M.C.). The present system, whereby money made available has to be spent in that year, would not be continued and the A.H.B. would have some initiative to spread their financial resources into subsequent years, in the interests of long-term planning. For this reason it is envisaged that the direct relationship with the Ministry that has always existed for the teaching hospitals be extended to all A.H.B.s, not just those which have a responsibility for a teaching hospital, so that it would be possible for the A.H.B. to liaise direct with the Ministry, if necessary, and not always make contact via the R.H.B. In this way the welfare services of the A.H.B., through having direct access to the Ministers of Welfare and Social Security, could feel assured that there would not be undue medical bias in the allocation of resources and that the welfare section would not become the Cinderella of the unified health service.

The A.H.B. would be advised by two senior officers—an executive director (also the secretary to the board) and a chief medical advisor. The latter may or may not be a full-time position, whereas his counterpart at R.H.B. level most certainly would be full time. In this way gifted medical men need not divorce themselves entirely from clinical work, in the same way that Oxford and Cambridge college masters do not relinquish their academic positions in order to assume the leadership of a college. It would also help to overcome what has become the traditional view in the medical profession that a colleague who enters such administrative avenues is a failure clinically. A similar approach is adopted in America for hospital administration, where the post may only be filled for a 5-year secondment period.

These two senior officers would attend all A.H.B. meetings and play active and equal roles in the discussion and decision-making activities. In addition the executive director would ultimately be responsible for the financial side of the board's activities, although assisted for that purpose by an assistant executive director (finance).

Linking the three present arms of the N.H.S. to work closely together involves more than an administrative adjustment and a feeling of goodwill and co-operation by all concerned. It is proposed that instead of dividing the services as now—hospital, local authority, and G.P.—or even by the simple division of in-patients and out-patients, that the service should be administered under three new heads. These would be:

      I.   Clinical services
     II.   Administrative services
    III.   Welfare services

The exact functions of each heading and its constituent services would need the most careful definition at local level in order to avoid a repetition of the present disharmony, which in part is a reflection of the lack of clear representation by all concerned of the other's functioning. For instance, the absence of a proper job specification for general practitioners has aggravated the problem of communications with hospitals, whilst at the same time hindering effective collaboration with local authority services. Modern medical care, with its multiplicity of specialities and ancillary workers, depends upon clear definitions of responsibility and this important factor should be borne in mind as a necessary adjunct to the administrative proposals.

Reference to Fig. 2 (p. 84) will show the extent to which these changes have transferred some existing services from their present settings. Basically, under heading (I) are to be found all the services for treatment, either institutional, consultative, or in the home. Each doctor can work within this framework, but in such a way that he offers the most effective service. A surgeon would normally only deal with hospital cases, but a paediatrician could function mostly within the consultative out-patient and domiciliary fields (as in the St. Mary's, London, scheme), using his in-patient facilities mainly for assessment and treatment in association with colleagues in other specialities where necessary.

The administrative services, heading (II), relate to the managerial and administrative aspects of the service; accommodation, administration, staffing, supplies, and financial control.

Welfare services, heading (III), bring together the various welfare and social workers, and offer a service for the sick that will harmonize or embrace a single social service unit.

Figure 2 shows various services, at present not formally linked, coming into a very close association. More particularly it shows the general practitioner formally integrated into the health service. The aim has been to reduce the present isolation and it is felt that, by working from health centres or community care units, and with the backing of the general medical services, this can be achieved. Also available on the same premises would be social workers and health visitors, with the centre or unit becoming responsible for the prevention of illness among all those registered with it, and for their care during illness. It would also be responsible for advising the mentally and physically handicapped and mobilizing the appropriate help and resources. Health visitors would continue to carry out preventive health duties, but could also assist and advise on the home treatment of illnesses and chronic conditions.

With social workers partly based on these units, the emphasis should be more on community medical social work than that

I. Clinical services	II. Administrative services	III. Welfare services
FUNCTIONS: Treatment and prevention	FUNCTIONS: Residential accommodation, facilities for clinics, equipment, etc.	FUNCTIONS: Social work and welfare, Welfare for sick, aged, and disabled in the community and their families
Surgery	Hospital accommodation for in-patient and out-patient care, and day hospitals	
Medicine		
Obstetrics, maternity	Other clinic facilities in community, including G.P.s surgeries	
Paediatrics		
School health	Hostels, nursing homes	Social work
Child guidance	Part III accommodation	Rehabilitation services
Psychiatry	Centres for occupational health	Sheltered workshops
General practice	Specialist clinics:	Meals on wheels
Dental care	Tuberculosis	Links to other welfare services, e.g.:
Preventive medicine	Ante-natal and post-natal	Child care
Public health	Dental surgeries, etc. (not necessarily in separate establishments)	Ministry of Social Security, etc.
	Health centres	
PERSONNEL:	Community care units	PERSONNEL:
Doctors	Ambulance services	Social workers, including those now hospital based, and those in local health authorities
Nurses, in-patient and community		
Ancillary medical staff:	PERSONNEL:	
Physiotherapists	Managerial, maintenance, clerical, etc.	
Pharmacists		
Pathology technicians, etc.		

FIGURE 2. STRUCTURE OF THE AREA HEALTH BOARD SERVICES

which exists in the present hospital-based service. It is of interest to note that in 1967 a joint department of social work was established by St. Francis' Hospital, London (a geriatric hospital in the King's College Teaching Hospital Group) and Southwark Council. The proposal was made so that effective social work could be undertaken in the community and hospital, and would also assist in the admission and discharge of patients.

Midwifery and maternity services are shown under the clinical heading, since the present divisions of care for maternity cases is one of the most unsatisfactory aspects of the present tripartite system. General practitioners on the obstetric list would work under the specialized supervision of the consultant.

The child guidance services are at present split three ways with regional hospital boards providing the psychiatrist, the local authority education department providing the psychologists, and the health and welfare department the remaining staff, including psychiatric social workers. There is rarely any backing by hospitals either for diagnostic aids, such as EEG recordings, or in-patient facilities for those who require it. The proposed structure, which would produce an integration between the local government services, the hospital, and the G.P., would not affect the close links between psychologists and schools. The remedial teachers could still be paid for and recruited by the education department of the local authority.

School health is in a very similar position, and the service is often provided on a sessional basis by G.P.s, which is unsatisfactory. The work calls for a knowledge of child development, children's diseases, child neurology and psychiatry, and ought to be one branch of a general paediatric service, including hospitals.

Although the Guillebaud Committee advised against the transfer to hospitals of the ambulance service, it is impossible to omit it from the new structure. The present problem of the hospitals, who are the major users, not being financially responsible would be overcome and the service ought thereby to benefit from a more efficient use. The Minister of Health has already decided to put this service under the existing regional hospital boards. In matters of day-to-day management the administrative officers of the A.H.B. should not be too restricted by directives received from above, otherwise they will become mere cyphers of the R.H.B. A positive effort to avoid the present discontent in the hospital administrative world must be made. One teaching hospital administrator has written of the "out-of-date management structure" and commented:

> When so much of trivial importance is being settled up and down the country by committees instead of individuals, when it is rare indeed to find hospital secretaries with worthwhile powers of spending money without referral, and when it is the exception rather than the rule that hospital officers of all types can dismiss as well as select staff, then it can be seen that in the present confines a great many administrative jobs are so narrow as to deprive them almost completely of the contents of satisfaction and positive attainment.[1]

Delegation, almost a first rule of successful managers, will therefore be essential, and on this will ultimately rest the calibre of the supporting staff recruited for the senior and middle-grade managerial posts. Delegation initially will be from the board to its three most senior assistant directors, administering the three sectors. One cannot be didactic about background qualifications, but initially, at least, it is possible to see a doctor in charge of clinical services; a lay administrator, perhaps an ex-hospital secretary, in charge of administrative services; and a person with a suitable professional background in charge of the welfare services.

Within each section there follows the middle-grade managers, heading the sub-sections. Thus the nursing services would be administered by a director of nursing (along the lines of the Salmon Report[2]), and the financial administration of the board undertaken by a treasurer, or executive council clerk. It would be unwise to try and define in detail the further subdivision of these units, into departments and spheres of responsibility. The exact blueprint must follow from the general acceptance of these ideas, and at the same time share in the genesis of ideas about management within the public sector currently stimulated by the Mallaby Committee's report on local government staffing.

Also we are pleased to note that the Welsh Regional Hospital Board's Staff Committee have commissioned the University College of South Wales to undertake a research project on "Patterns of Management in the Proposed District General Hospitals".

It is, however, appropriate to sketch out the tentative conclusions on the managerial structure we would ideally favour. At the outset there is the double handicap of applying management theory because we are proposing partially lay boards, who will determine objectives, and because of the considerable organizational complexity found in hospital and health organizations. No easy parallels may be drawn from other fields and no blueprint for success obtained from I.C.I. or big industry. In hospitals, for example, there is a conflict in objectives between the need for giving first priority to patients and the training requirements for future generations of doctors and nurses. There is the immense problem of communication between the many specialities, ancillary occupational groups, and the varied terminologies and expertise used. Added to this is the existence of hierarchies and authoritarian traditions governing relationships between staff, and the concept of clinical freedom so strongly entrenched in British medicine. It is not surprising therefore that academic interest in the organization of hospitals, whilst late in creation, has been largely confined to sociologists and social psychologists, and that the discussion on managerial techniques has only been stimulated since the middle 1960's.

Nevertheless, management techniques can still be applied with success in the new structure we envisage. The executive officer will have the task of creating the conditions which will bring about the optimum use of all resources available in the Service. His scope is clearly wide—from the technical to the more intangible like "morale", with the administrative problems presented by the diverse organization as an added factor. Above all it will be his task to build up the whole into a team, with a working pattern and unified output. Modern management has to perform this task and thus far there is a similarity between the new structure and industry. More important, successful business has shown that these seemingly ideal objectives are not impossible to achieve, and the results of their experience are available for translation into the health service. The absence of an equivalent to "managing director" in either hospitals or local health authorities, combined with the dominance of lay committees, has prevented the application of these techniques hitherto.

These arrangements should also mark the end of the present malaise already referred to above, where able graduate recruits in both hospitals and local authorities are frustrated by the inability to exercise any proper function. Rosemary Stevens has summarized the position aptly in relation to hospital administrators:

> Hospitals are entering a new era. The pattern of administration is lagging behind. At present, management or specialist functions are not isolated from other administrative or clerical functions. Until they are, the status of hospital administration in relation to other professions, especially the medical profession, is unlikely appreciably to rise above its present indeterminate state—varying, according to the individual, from a jobbing clerk, through the status of a loyal retainer, to a highly sophisticated expert. The effectiveness of tomorrow's hospitals rests more than a little on finding a solution to these problems.[3]

The proposals which we make would offer a valid career structure for administrators; recruitment for A.H.B. posts would come from the lower levels of administration at the local level and in turn preference would be given to the most able A.H.B. administrators for recruitment to the R.H.B. positions.

As an example, the managerial line of command in one of the district general hospitals under an A.H.B. will illustrate our theme. It is important to remember that the district general hospital will be providing between 600 and 800 beds, employing a staff of over four figures and spending approximately £2 million per annum. Within its complex will be the need for a general manager, responsible for his budget, distribution of funds available, purchase of supplies, hiring and firing of staff, consideration of new services, efficiency, morale, and acting as a local communications link within the new framework of health services as well as within his own hospital. He should not have to refer to a higher authority, as at present, applications for unpaid maternity leave, or refunds of training course fees (one item for 75 per cent of £1 11s. 0d. was recently dealt with by the Ministry of Health after it had been approved by a management committee), or wait while samples of a tender for sausages are dealt with by various committees and sub-committees. Instead he must, in turn, delegate defined responsibilities to other staff members. The report produced jointly by the King Edward's Hospital Fund and the Institute of Hospital Administrators offers a useful blueprint.[4] This report brings to the aid of the general manager four directors of service: medical and para-medical services, nursing services, finance and statistical services and general services (hotel, personnel, engineering services). From Fig. 2 it will be seen that our proposals give the directors of medical and nursing services responsibilities outside the hospital as well. This concept, with its clearly defined general manager as the senior officer, marks the end of the other tripartite structure within the health service—defined by the Bradbeer Committee Report in 1954,[5] which saw the internal administration of hospitals as being composed of three parts: medical, nursing, and lay administration, forming a "blended team". This scheme, without a leader and depending upon informal and undefined roles, has never worked and is certainly not the pattern most suitable for the district general hospitals of the future. The Kings Fund/I.H.A. Report comments: "Shortage of money is chronic, and the need is to make the best of what is available by efficiency in administration of men as well as money. A sound management structure is essential to achieve this and we hope to have suggested one."

We believe that they are correct, and that viewed within the context of the A.H.B. unified structure, their scheme would be of considerable benefit and importance.

CHAPTER 9

Proposals for the General Practitioner and Community Services

THE problems posed by the present structure for the organization of general practice has been described in previous chapters. The prime need is to integrate G.P.s with the domiciliary nursing services, with health visitors, and social workers, and to ensure that they have easy access to the kind of diagnostic facilities now available only in hospitals.

The health centre is intended as a way of tackling one aspect of this problem, namely to achieve closer liaison between G.P.s and the local authority services. The health centre will also enable doctors to work in larger groups than at present, and facilitate the employment of secretaries and receptionists, thus freeing the doctor from administrative duties. However, this is only one side of the problem and does not deal at all with the question of the relationship between hospitals and community workers.

With the development of preventive medicine and the control of acute and infectious diseases, the pattern of illness in the country is changing. Many conditions formerly dealt with mainly in hospital, such as children's diseases, are now more commonly dealt with at home. At the same time there has been a clear shift in morbidity from acute to chronic illness of the kind which requires lengthy treatment, and this is best given in close co-operation with existing community medical and nursing services.

It seems essential, therefore, that the work of hospital out-patient departments be allied more closely to the work of those doctors and nurses who are responsible for the care of the patient in his own home. Conversely, the G.P. requires greater contact with the hospital so that he can make use of essential hospital equipment, benefit from the stimulus of interaction with specialists, and learn about new developments in treatment.

We must ensure that the G.P. be provided with the type of work situation which will allow him to make much better use of nursing services and other ancillary help. G.P.s at present waste far too much time on purely clerical functions or on minor complaints which could be dealt with quite efficiently by a competent nurse. A two-man practice which has employed a part-time nurse for 9 months found that the nurse could cope effectively with over one-third of requests for visits and that this was quite satisfactory to the patient. Patients, of course, retained the right of direct access to the doctor if they so wished. Within surgery time, the nurse also took over many of the routine testing and preventative treatments, e.g. immunization, which G.P.s normally do alone. In this way the practice was able to cope with a list of 5500 patients with much greater efficiency and ease. [1]

Although there has been an increase in the proportion of G.P.s who work in partnerships rather than single-handed practices, it is still only a small minority of doctors who work in well co-ordinated groups of six or more practitioners. Furthermore, although there has recently been a marked increase in the building of health centres and the Ministry of Health has suggested that plans for 300 centres by 1976 may be greatly exceeded, in 10 years' time there will still be less than 10 per cent of G.P.s working in such premises.

Another disturbing factor in the present situation is that plans to expand hospital facilities and local authority schemes to build new clinics and health centres are frequently being developed in isolation without any attempt to co-ordinate or to consider whether shared facilities would be more appropriate. The use of joint premises might well produce direct financial benefits, but, more important, would allow a more economic use of trained personnel and specialized equipment, both of which are in short supply.

The most urgent need is to insist that the siting of all future health centres should become immediately a joint responsibility of the local authority and the regional hospital board. This decision simply cannot wait for reorganization, for we are in grave danger of developing a series of health centres which have little relationship to any planned community health service.

Where they are sited near to the hospital out-patient departments, health centres need not attempt to provide the complete range of diagnostic facilities provided that there is full liaison with the hospital services, and that they at least bring together the G.P. and the existing local authority health and welfare services. This is the way that the best health centres are developing at present, but we must accept that to achieve full integration with local authority staff, including social workers, and with hospital consultant services it will be necessary to centralize rather more. This means that a larger number of practitioners will operate from the same premises than is common at present, and patients may therefore have to travel a little further for a consultation. The idea of the health centre has now won pretty wide acceptance after a very long delay, but it would be unfortunate if the development of a community health service stopped at conventional health centres. The health centre is, after all, a pre-war concept and the fact that it has taken 30 years to become a reality does not mean that this pattern should be sacrosanct for all time.

It is true that doctors working in health centres sited close to hospitals could more easily make use of the hospital's diagnostic facilities, particularly if both hospitals and health centres were financed and administered by the same authority. However, we should consider whether a more radical approach would not be more appropriate for the full integration of community and hospital services.

The standard design of health centres does not at present include diagnostic equipment such as X-ray apparatus. Indeed, it would be pointless if it did, for there are at present quite insufficient numbers of technicians to operate diagnostic equipment in so many units. Furthermore, health centres are not generally planned to include specialist out-patient sessions, let alone out-patient surgery. The current plans for hospital building are based on the concept of a "district general hospital" which has about 600–800 beds and serves a population of 100,000–150,000. These developments and plans indicate that although the G.P. will increasingly be housed in purpose-built premises which will also accommodate local health authority staff, he will still be quite separate from hospital buildings and from their staff. Current ideas about contacts between general practitioners and hospitals mainly concern clinical assistant posts or visits to hospitals by G.P.s either to see their patients or simply to meet staff on social occasions such as morning coffee. It should be noted that the post of clinical assistant is clearly junior to that of a specialist and the staffing of hospitals by this means is therefore expensive, since G.P.s are now among the highest paid medical staff.

There has been remarkably little discussion of how general-practice buildings relate to local hospitals. Health centres can unite general practice and local health authority services, but hospital services are usually left in a separate compartment. The N.H.S. has not only a tripartite administrative structure, but a tripartite geographical distribution. Ideas about planning have become over-concentrated upon replacing buildings without sufficient examination of the functions which these buildings must now house. The collective rate of capital investment for the rebuilding of hospitals, general-practice premises and local health authority clinics will only be satisfactory provided that there is a more functional programme of rebuilding.

The realization that the funds likely to be available for future health services are strictly limited has led to deep depression about the possibility of improvement. What has been totally lacking from most discussion of the development of health services is the notion of increasing productivity. It has been assumed that doctors, nurses, and other workers would be unable to become more efficient in the way in which they provided services and therefore unable to do more in the same amount of time without sacrificing quality. By avoiding wasteful duplication of services such as exists in the different areas of overlap between hospital, local authority, G.P., and occupational health services, skilled manpower could obviously be saved. Furthermore, instead of at least three separate programmes of development for medical buildings, e.g. hospitals, health centres and group practice buildings, and local health authority clinics, the joint use of premises and services could provide more—for less cost. More rational use of buildings would catalyse the delegation of simple tasks still being carried out by expensively trained staff. There are no *a priori* reasons for health services being incapable of improving efficiency and productivity.

The pattern of development outlined in a recent *Lancet* article suggests a way that services could be developed in the future which would allow for much closer integration of G.P.s, community workers, and hospitals, and make more efficient use of resources. [2] It is argued that we should re-examine the concept of the district general hospital. The Ministry is at present committed to this concept which envisages the development of hospitals designed to provide the full range of in-patient and out-patient facilities for the catchment population. Wherever possible it is intended to site these hospitals close to the main population centre. However, it is not easy to obtain central sites for hospitals of this size and in any case locating all services in the district general hospital will inevitably mean longer journeys for patients than they usually have at present. This is not likely to prove too inconvenient for in-patients, but will cause problems for out-patients. The article suggests that we should consider whether it would be possible to disperse the hospital out-patient facilities and combine these with the already accepted proposals for health centres.

The proposed units, which the *Lancet* article calls community care units, would be designed to serve a population of about 50,000, and would house about 20–25 G.P.s. Since the majority of the population lives in urban areas of 50,000 or more, this would mean that in most towns no one would live more than a mile from such a unit. It is clear that the need for the suggested community care units as opposed to the more conventional community surgeries will largely depend on factors such as geography and population. It has something very real to offer where new hospitals have to be built on the edge of the town because of the shortage of land in the city centre. It is here where one really does see the foolishness of holding on to the old concept of linking out-patient and in-patient facilities, involving much travelling for the patients, considerable inconvenience, and an artificial separation from the G.P. Equally, where a small or medium-sized hospital is already sited in the centre of a community it would be absurd to remove from it all its out-patient facilities. What is needed is a flexible attitude which tailors the health services to the community, not as so frequently in the past, the community to the health service.

The scheme has a number of advantages. In the first place it would mean that the district general hospital itself would not have to have such a large central site, and that out-patients would not have so far to travel. More important perhaps would be the opportunity offered for G.P.s and hospital doctors to work together in the same premises. This would allow for much closer contact to the benefit of both parties, and since this unit would contain the usual out-patient diagnostic facilities, would give the G.P. a better clinical setting for his own work.

It should be emphasized that housing so many G.P.s in the same building in no sense means that they have to work as one partnership or group. Within each unit, doctors could operate in small teams. Even with existing health centres it is quite common for doctors to be organized in two or more separate partnerships although they all share the same facilities. We envisage that different sub-groups of doctors within such a structure would be organized in teams which would include district nurses, health visitors, domiciliary midwives, and, as at present, the doctors would be responsible for particular areas of the population although it would be convenient to have more "zoning" of patients than occurs at present in most towns.

The general pattern of the medical services would therefore be modified district general hospitals primarily for in-patients requiring only short-stay care and for casualty cases. Patients living in their own homes would be cared for from the community care unit, which would combine health centre and out-patient facilities, and provide the full range of community services, including home nursing and home helps. The chronic sick who require temporary or permanent in-patient facilities would be housed in smaller units which could provide a more homely atmosphere than could the hospitals. Standards of care for the chronic units would be maintained by operating them under the same administration as the district general hospital, which would provide consultant cover, and would share medical, nursing staff, and other facilities. It would be important to avoid allowing the chronic units to become professional backwaters, but this could be achieved by rotating district general hospital staff through these units to prevent any isolation from the main hospital.

The community care units would be a new kind of institution but would most resemble a combination of a health centre or large group practice and an out-patient department. Specialists from the hospital, which could deal predominantly with in-patients, would see out-patients and undertake out-patient surgery in these units on a sessional basis. This is where varicose veins and hernias could be operated on for those patients suitable for community care. Day care for geriatric and psychiatric patients would preferably be provided in the community care unit, though there should be no aim to produce anything resembling a cottage hospital. The optimum sizes of the units could be worked out by trials in different areas.

Common diagnostic procedures such as simple radiography and basic pathology would be available in the community units, either provided on the spot at specific sessions or by effective linkage with the hospital. Local health authority clinic and nursing services would be based in the community care units, as would some social services. Preventive medicine services such as health education and screening examinations and tests would be based in community care units, although preventive health campaigns would be planned and organized by specialist units often at a regional or a national level.

The hospitals would house those services for which centralization is absolutely necessary according to current ideas. Thus, accident centres, major anaesthetic and surgery services which have to be provided on a 24 hour basis, would be found in the hospital. Most, but not all, in-patient care in the district would be found within the hospital at least if quick access to relatively scarce services was needed. Out-patient care for chronic patients of various kinds would be community based with medical cover from the community care units. The scale of in-patient care in the hospital would be significantly lower than traditional levels because of the expansion of community and day care, and this should reduce costs.

Rare clinical specialities such as cardiothoracic surgery would be provided in special regional or sub-regional hospitals. Service units such as those for laundry, sterilization and special pathology would serve several community care units and hospitals and they would be sited in relation to transport systems. The kind of development which we propose fits the concept of *a complex of specialized health service units*. Traditional divisions of our health services in terms of "hospital and community" or "hospital and general practice" ossify thinking, and do not generally reflect needs. In summary, units along the lines which we propose would provide better services for general practice because of the provision of diagnostic equipment and the better contact with specialists, and they would provide more economical services because of the closer collaboration between the currently separate branches.

There may be strong arguments for basing some professional social work services in community care units although there would be a danger of making them less approachable because of too close association with a clinical atmosphere. However, there would certainly be every reason for arranging effective liaison between community care units and social services.

This or any other kind of proposal for shaping health services along functional rather than traditional lines implies certain general patterns of organization. The planning of buildings has to be carried out by bodies which cover all branches of the services. At present we have three separate building programmes but comprehensive planning demands the same financial source. The provision of health services should not be bogged down in questions of squalid competition to avoid expenditure on this building because it would be "on the rates" or that building because it would be from the hospital board. The capital equipment of the health service should be provided in accordance with needs and general resources.

Although the proposal for community care units would give a much earlier prospect of rehousing and integrating general practice, public health and many hospital specialist services, we are not suggesting the immediate and wholesale adoption of this plan. Even if only one per cent of the current capital investment of the N.H.S. were devoted to trials of this and other schemes, it would soon be possible to develop reliable and general plans.

CHAPTER 10

Mental Health Services Proposals

CHAPTER 5 described the present system of organization for the mental health services. To recap, in brief, patients in the community are mainly the responsibility of the local health authority, which aims to provide for the welfare and training needs of patients. The medical treatment of patients living at home is shared between some combination of the local authority medical officer for mental health, the G.P., and hospital doctors working in out-patient departments. Patients requiring detailed assessment or intensive clinical care are referred to hospital together with the majority of patients requiring residential care, whether this is for medical or social reasons. In-patient services are based mainly on the large comprehensive psychiatric hospital. This pattern of responsibility was developed at a time when there were only rudimentary services available in the community, and the patient who remained at home received little or no care unless he became a serious problem. In this case he was admitted to hospital where he tended to remain indefinitely since there were few medical or other treatments available and so little prospect for improvement or cure.

At present approximately 60 per cent of patients diagnosed as mentally ill are in hospital, while 40 per cent are cared for within the community. Forty per cent of sub-normal patients are in hospital and 60 per cent are living in the community. Some hostel, nursing, or foster care is provided by the local authority, but only for a very limited number of patients. Only 3 per cent of the mentally ill and 4·5 per cent of the mentally sub-normal living in the community are provided with residential accommodation. [1] It is estimated that many of the patients in hospitals for the mentally ill and over half in hospitals for the mentally sub-normal are resident primarily for reasons other than their psychiatric treatment needs. [2]

What this means, in effect, is that many patients who cannot benefit from intensive hospital treatment are in hospital only because they require residential care. This is because either they have no family or their families are unable to provide adequate supervision. In addition, even patients who need active treatment may not necessarily require full hospitalization if the family can accept some responsibility for their care, or if alternative residential accommodation were available. This is not to argue that all patients who do not absolutely require it should ideally be removed from psychiatric hospitals. However, it is now apparent that other forms of care could be applied to such patients with beneficial effects, depending on the needs of the individual patient, the siting of the psychiatric hospital, and the range of facilities which it can provide. Patients in active treatment as well as patients for whom this no longer seems appropriate may require training or rehabilitation whether the patient lives in hospital, in a hostel, or at home. All patients, both in-patients and out-patients, and their families require social and welfare services. Finally, many patients, particularly the mentally ill, require alternating periods of residential or community care, either because their mental state varies or because the family situation changes. It is difficult to avoid the conclusion that the strict division of function between the local authority and the hospital is now quite inappropriate to meet patient needs and the administrative structure must, therefore, be re-tailored to fit the kind of treatment patterns and services which can now be provided.

Recognition of this fact has led to some local experiments which attempt to bridge the gap between G.P., local authority, and hospital services. These schemes have usually arisen because the hospital psychiatrists felt dissatisfied with the way referrals were made and because of the problems of discharging patients without a full knowledge of the community background. In all parts of the country, hospital admission for the mentally ill increased rapidly during the 1950's, partly as a result of the increased use of voluntary admission and partly because of the new treatment procedures which encouraged G.P.s to refer patients earlier in the course of their illness. In some cases, hospital admissions increased to such an extent that psychiatrists were forced to review in-patients for discharge but found that effective discharge could not be achieved without the co-operation of the local authority and the G.P. These schemes, therefore, have tended to be somewhat hospital oriented in that they were initiated by the hospital and tend to use the hospital as a base from which other services have developed.

These schemes all report success at least in the sense that most of the officers involved feel subjectively that improved co-operation has produced better working conditions and higher morale. Where objective methods have been applied to measure success in terms of patient improvement or satisfaction by families, claims are rather more conservative, but nevertheless encouraging.

In one area, Chichester, [3] the local psychiatric hospital attempted to get better liaison with G.P.s in order to encourage domiciliary consultation between the G.P. and specialists. At the same time, additional out-patient clinic sessions were provided both at the psychiatric hospital and at the general hospital in the area. Day hospitals were added to the psychiatric hospitals, sharing training facilities, etc., with the parent hospital. The aim of the scheme was to improve facilities for care outside hospital through the extension of out-patient or day hospital services and through domiciliary care under the G.P., in order to limit the number of patients admitted to hospital and to allow earlier discharge.

Evaluation studies showed that this scheme did, indeed, lead to more contacts between G.P.s and psychiatrists, both in terms of an increased number of referrals and the number of domiciliary consultations and also through G.P.s seeking advice on treatment. By operating such services it was found possible to reduce the number of patients admitted to hospital, although the total volume of referrals increased. The additional referrals consisted mainly of patients with depressive illnesses and senile mental conditions rather than neurotics, that is, more severely ill patients were referred rather than more patients with milder conditions. Comparison with a similar area, Salisbury, which was operating more conservative services, showed that while 52 per cent of all referrals were admitted to hospital in Salisbury, only 14 per cent were admitted in Chichester. Patients tended to be referred earlier in the course of illness and more patients in the lower social classes were referred than in Salisbury. Chichester tended to use admission mostly for aged or single patients, for patients with organic conditions or for seriously disturbed functional psychotics. Married patients, patients in employment, and patients with depressive conditions were less likely to be hospitalized in the Chichester area.

When the burden on the family was considered, there was little difference between the two areas. That is, even though fewer patients were admitted in the Chichester area, families did not report significantly higher rates of problems resulting from the patient's illness. This is not to imply that all was well, since of families exhibiting severe problems, 40 per cent did not report relief within either type of service. In particular, families caring for senile relatives or relatives with organic conditions, reported continuing problems even when domiciliary treatment was provided. Nevertheless, this study does show that positive advantages can be gained if constructive attempts are made to integrate community and hospital services.

A scheme at Plymouth tackled the problem in a rather different way by building a special centre within the town as a result of joint consultation between the hospital and the local authority. [4] The centre provided accommodation for integrated social work, a day hospital, social clubs, and consulting rooms. A child guidance clinic was also attached. Special staff were appointed either from local authority or hospital sources, and most medical staff from the hospital were also employed at the clinic on a sessional basis. Delays in starting the centre occurred because the local authority found the scheme rather unorthodox, at least with respect to the idea of integrated social work and having children and adults treated in the same building. Furthermore, the staffing ratios originally agreed upon could not be provided from the beginning because of lack of funds. The result of the evaluation study must be read with these problems in mind, therefore, because the evaluation occurred before the scheme could be said to be properly underway.

The evaluation study compared the patterns of referral and admission for the first 2 years following the setting up of the clinic, with the 2 years previously. Only limited success could be reported at the time of the follow-up. The number of patients referred for psychiatric consultation by the local authority increased once the clinic was set up, due presumably to the improved contact between mental welfare officers and psychiatrists. There was a slight reduction in the amount of time spent in hospital over a 2-year period and there was an increased number of out-patient psychiatric sessions. One reason suggested why results were not more dramatic was that it takes some time for psychiatric and other staff to adapt to new facilities for treating patients. They do not so readily alter their habits, that changes can be demonstrated within a short period of providing new types of services, and therefore only a longer period of follow-up could demonstrate fully the beneficial effects of this scheme.

A third example is available from Nottingham, where, ever since 1948 there have been joint appointments between the hospital and the local authority. The physician superintendent of the hospital is also the medical officer for mental health, and other hospital psychiatrists and social workers are also integrated into the local authority services. Nursing staff are seconded for short periods to the social work department so that they can gain more insight into the community aspects of illness and treatment. Out-patient clinics are provided together with a geriatric day centre.

The evaluation study [5] compared the outcome for schizophrenic patients admitted to this hospital, with the outcome for similar patients admitted to two other hospitals where more traditional services were provided. The study showed that over a 5-year period the total length of time spent in hospital by the Nottingham patients was rather less than for patients admitted to the two other hospitals. However, although in Nottingham the length of the first admission was shorter than in the more conservative hospitals, the numbers requiring a second admission were the same, and there were a larger number of subsequent re-admissions. When the discharged patients were compared, it was found that Nottingham patients living in the community showed just as many symptoms and evidence of disturbed behaviour as patients discharged from the comparison hospitals, despite the fact that services in Nottingham were oriented towards "community care". In other words patients were living at home with severe symptoms in all three areas and families were having to cope with very difficult and distressing situations. In none of the areas were the services providing adequate support for the discharged patient or his family.

Other studies by the same research team have analysed the factors which seemed to produce relapse in patients and were able to demonstrate that where patients were living at home in a highly charged emotional atmosphere, or where patients were unable to find employment, the chances of re-admission were very high. [6, 7] However good the contact is between hospital and community services, it is still necessary to examine what specific services in the community have to be amplified if integration is to be successful. It would appear from these studies that provision of lodgings or hostels and developing more employment opportunities would achieve greater success than frequent home visits by sympathetic case-workers.

These studies suggest that integration between hospital and domiciliary services is administratively possible and that all officers find this is a more satisfactory approach. Although only limited success can be reported in terms of improvement in the patient or in the family situation, this seems to be due mainly to the fact that these schemes involve only the partial integration of services. In particular they are all largely hospital based and aimed to reduce admissions or to cut down length of stay, and perhaps do not consider fully the specific ways community services must develop if the patient is to be maintained satisfactorily outside the hospital and his family is to be given adequate relief. No scheme fully involves both G.P.s and the local health authority with the hospital authority, each attempts to bridge only one administrative barrier, and none tries to integrate the psychiatric services with the other medical services.

It seems probable that a more radical administrative reform might be more satisfactory than these piece-meal arrangements; one which did not simply graft community services onto the hospital but truly integrated in-patient and domiciliary care.

Under the unified administrative structure described in Chapter 7, the mental health services could be integrated with the general medical services, operating as far as possible under the area health board (A.H.B.), from district general hospitals, and community care units. Planning at regional health board (R.H.B.) level would try to ensure an even spread of services throughout the region so that each A.H.B. could provide the full range of psychiatric services. Each A.H.B. would be responsible for providing services for the mentally disordered within its catchment area, on the same basis as for other conditions.

The "clinical services" section would be responsible for providing psychiatric nurses and doctors for both in-patients and community-based patients; the "administrative section" would be responsible for providing residential accommodation of varying kinds together with day hospitals and out-patient facilities. This accommodation would be integrated where appropriate with the accommodation provided for other conditions, e.g. out-patient sessions might be provided at the A.H.B. community care unit or health centres. The "welfare services" section would provide social workers who would work on a local basis, and be responsible for all patients in one area, whether these patients lived at home or on one of the residential units. Training services would be provided in a similar way, that is services would be organized on a geographical basis, and both in-patients and out-patients would attend the same centres, as far as this was possible, with additional facilities in residential units only for those patients unable to travel out daily to the training centre.

Residential Services

It should be possible to examine the hospital services at present provided and to distinguish between those patients requiring simply a residential service and those requiring psychiatric or medical in-patient treatment. This has been attempted for sub-normals in the Birmingham area and in the Wessex Region. The findings from these two areas are likely to reflect needs which would be found throughout the country as a whole.

This kind of division would allow for a more efficient use of the limited medical and psychiatric in-patient services available. The following categories of residential centres could be deduced.

(1) Psychiatric units for assessment and intensive treatment. These units would be attached to the district general hospital when these are in operation, but meanwhile, where there is no room for psychiatric wards in the general hospitals in the imme-diate future, they could be sited separately while remaining under the same administration as the general hospital, sharing staff and facilities with the parent hospital. These units would also provide the basis for the out-patient medical services.

(2) Intensive care units for geriatric patients or very handi-capped severely sub-normal patients who require total nursing care. These would be under the supervision of a specialist doctor, who need not be resident, but day-to-day care could be provided by the ordinary medical services, for example G.P.s.

These units would be mainly for long-stay patients who would require a different kind of accommodation to that provided for the patients in district general hospitals, who would be mainly short-stay cases. Although these units must be attached to the general hospital in order to share their clinical staff and facilities, it would probably be best to site them separately. Most units would be fairly small, especially if they housed children, so that a more intimate atmosphere could be provided. These units could also provide short-stay care for similar patients who live with their families, but who need in-patient care in times of family crises or simply to give families temporary relief.

(3) Residential units and hostels for patients who do not need intensive psychiatric or medical care, but who for social or other reasons cannot be returned to the community. The size of these units could vary, but again preferably would be small. Like the intensive care units they would best be sited away from the general hospital, but in or near urban centres to allow for maximum interaction between the patient and the community. Patients resident in these units could then share in community services such as training centres and the aim would be to rehabilitate as many as possible back to the community. Psychiatric cover should be provided but psychiatrists need not be resident and a nursing or lay administrator could run the unit. These units would provide both short-stay and long-stay care.

(4) Some provision would also be necessary for patients who are physically ill or have some chronic disability such as tuberculosis, but these should be cared for in the general hospitals like all other patients with the same conditions, except in occasional circumstances.

It must be emphasized that although some of these units would be most appropriately sited away from the district general hospital, they should be under the same general administration so that maximum integration could obtain. Units for long-stay patients must not be allowed to become isolated in any practical sense from the main active treatment centres, and there must be a system for the sharing of staff and facilities between the general medical services of the district general hospital and these residential annexes.

In the immediate future, of course, most patients will continue to be housed in the same over-large inappropriate accommodation as at present, since it will be impossible to scrap the present psychiatric hospitals and build new premises for some time.

However, it should be possible to reorganize existing structures on this basis, which would at least rationalize residential services and deploy specialized manpower more efficiently, and in addition help to pin-point the patients' main problems and needs. An article in the *Lancet*[8] describes a reorganization on these lines for a 2000 bedded hospital for the mentally ill. Like most psychiatric hospitals this was composed of a series of units of varying sizes which could be utilised to provide separate premises for the different needs of patients.

The approximate division obtained was as follows:

(1) Admission unit for intensive psychiatric care, 220 beds in a separate building.
(2) A geriatric unit, 800 beds, some in separate buildings but most in wards in the main hospital.
(3) Long-stay unit, 830 beds. Some of these patients were, in fact, mentally sub-normal.
(4) Physically sick (mostly chronic) 80 beds in a detached building.

This kind of reorganization, therefore, is no pipe-dream which could only occur given unlimited funds and brand new premises. While ideally new and smaller units would be preferable, existing hospitals could meanwhile be adapted successfully. The *Lancet* paper claimed that this reorganization did result in a more efficient use of specialized medical and nursing resources, which could then be concentrated on those most in need.

However, it is also true that even within the next few years regional boards are planning to improve psychiatric in-patient facilities and these schemes could be incorporated into the type of pattern which we are proposing. In fact, Wessex, which is noted for being one of the most progressive of the R.H.B.s, is already seeking to operate family group homes for sub-normal children requiring residential care, and these will be provided on a local basis (i.e. approximately 20 beds for population units of 100,000). Liaison with the local health authorities has resulted in their promise to provide extra places in their training centres, so that these children will be able to attend on the same basis as children with similar handicaps living at home. [9]

Training and Education

Both in-patients and patients living in the community have similar training and education needs so there is no rational basis for organizing these separately, especially since hospitals do not seem able to provide these services very efficiently. The aim of these services is to help patients to become as independent as possible. All patients who can do so will then return to normal community life, to work, if not to live. The remaining patients must continue to work in a sheltered environment, but they can be taught satisfying and productive work.

For young adults and children schooling should be provided in conjunction with the education department if this can be arranged. There is no good reason why the education of subnormal children should be undertaken solely by the health department, as at present. Schools or training centres for children and young adults may be sited at the residential centres or in the community, but in either case should be shared by both in-patients and community-based patients.

For adult patients a series of graded workshops are required which vary from sheltered workshops for patients who are incapable of working elsewhere, to factory units on industrial estates which would prepare patients for jobs in a normal industrial setting. The former Middlesex Mental Health Department used to run a service which would provide a very good model for training schemes based on this approach. Again patients in any of the various types of clinical or residential units should attend the same workshops and training centres as patients living at home.

Existing facilities could be reorganized on this pattern, but in any case both local authorities and hospitals are planning to expand their training facilities, and new provision could be sited with the needs of both in-patients and community patients in mind. At present facilities for hospital patients and patients living at home are not usually co-ordinated even when there is an opportunity to do so. For example, recently one large mental sub-normality hospital in the Home Counties built a brand new school for in-patients, while half a mile away, on a site bordering on the hospital grounds, a similar purpose-built unit was erected by the local authority for their children. Plans to co-ordinate facilities were considered but under the present system the administrative and political obstacles to sharing building and running costs were too great to make this possible.

Social and Welfare Services

Most psychiatric patients and their families need additional social and welfare services. These are at present provided for hospital patients by psychiatric social workers and by local authority mental welfare officers for patients living at home. There is inevitably some duplication of functions between hospital and community social workers, therefore, which could be avoided if there were not two separate services. In addition it has been pointed out that although hospital psychiatric social workers are the more highly trained, their work tasks are less exacting than those of the mental welfare officers who are relatively poorly trained. [10, 11] Mental welfare officers have the very difficult job of assessing patients for admission and of coping with family problems when the patient is discharged or being treated as an out-patient. The psychiatric social worker has the more limited task of preparing patients and their families for discharge, but by the confines of the present system, she cannot adequately follow up her cases into the community. This division of responsibility is clearly unsatisfying for the social worker and is not satisfactory for the patient either, since he passes between different kinds of social work personnel at different stages in his treatment. It also produces duplication of work and an inefficient use of the limited trained personnel available.

It would be interesting to know why the more highly trained

social workers prefer to work in a hospital setting. It seems likely that liaison with the psychiatrist and the feeling of being part of a treatment team is the most imprtant factor. The mental welfare officer by contrast is divorced from contact with medical and nursing personnel and works in relative isolation from all other agencies involved in treatment.

Analysis of the kind of work undertaken by mental welfare officers reveals wide differences between areas, partly depending on the number of mental welfare officers available and partly on the way that mental health services are organized in any particular area, for example the amount of contact between G.P. and hospital consultants or the extent of hospital out-patient facilities. In some areas mental welfare officers are used primarily as the agent between G.P.s and the specialized treatment services, especially when admission to hospital seems necessary. While this is a basic function of the mental welfare officer it is hardly very satisfying if this kind of work occupies most of her time. When mental welfare officer interviews were assessed in terms of content, most of these were concerned with "practical matters" and relatively few with "inter-personal problems". However, over half of all interviews were initiated by the mental welfare officers themselves suggesting that they have a greater degree of autonomy than is usual for hospital-based social workers. Very few interviews could be regarded as constituting true "casework". (12)

Under the new administrative system proposed, one type of psychiatric social worker could be substituted. These would be organized on a local basis serving particular areas, as, for example, health visitors are at present. Each social worker would follow up her cases throughout the course of the illness, maintain contact if the patient needed admission, and help in rehabilitation when he was discharged. She would have regular sessions in the intensive clinical units where patients would be admitted for treatment, which would allow her to gain contact with psychiatric and nursing staff and attend case conferences for her own patients. Her main work, however, would be with patients living at home or in the other local residential units. Her main base would, therefore, be the community care unit or health centre, where she would have contact with G.P.s, psychiatrists undertaking out-patient sessions, and other social work and nursing staff also operating from the community care units. She would be able, in this setting, to maintain liaison with the other welfare services so that these could be made readily available for psychiatric patients.

It has been pointed out that at present we do not make full use of the special skills of psychiatric nurses in the care of the discharged patient.

> Much of her skill is developed by trial and error after long experience, and it seems wasteful for it to be confined to brief periods while the patient is in hospital, particularly since the behaviour which requires skilled nursing care so often continues after discharge. [5]

It would be of great value to have a psychiatric nurse working together with a social worker at the community care unit so that her advice could be sought on those matters which are essentially practical nursing problems, and with which, at the moment, families have to cope alone or without adequate guidance. It might also be useful to have some interchange of staff during training periods so that both social workers and nurses could learn more about each other's roles and problems. Again the present division between in-patients and out-patients care makes this kind of interchange difficult to achieve.

This type of organization would allow "continuity of care" to become a reality instead of merely wishful thinking as it so often is at present. It would also have the advantage of providing medical staff with better information than is currently possible about the patient's home conditions and his behaviour outside a sheltered ward environment.

Conclusions

The greater proportion of patients in England and Wales who are suffering from some kind of mental disorder are living in the community, the majority with their families. However, at present, services are still concentrated on hospital patients. These may well be most in need, but it is obvious from the studies quoted that at the moment there is an uneven distribution of resources between community-based patients and hospital-based patients. Patients are being discharged into the community without proper provision being made for their care, and this results in repeated re-admission and a great deal of misery and hardship for the family and the patient alike. "We are transferring the care of the mentally ill from trained staff to untrained or ill-equipped staff or no staff at all". [13] Mental health services organized in the fashion we suggest would achieve a better orientation towards the problems of patients living at home.

One eminent psychiatrist has summarized the basic issues for a community care programme as follows.

> The first essential is an active list of patients needing community care, discharge from which would require the same careful consideration as discharge from mental hospital. A patient should never be allowed to fall out of care by mistake. This presupposes a complex system of recording the domiciliary visits of staff and the attendances of patients so that what *is* happening can be constantly compared with what *ought* to be happening. [5]

He also points out that the patient has to re-approach the community via two "ladders"—one domestic and the other occupational. Any one patient may progress along each route at a different rate. Hence it is necessary to provide a graded series of residential and occupational opportunities ranging from a totally sheltered environment to a normal one, such that it is possible for the patient to traverse each route at a separate pace.

It would seem almost essential to reorganize services on a geographical basis in order to achieve these objectives. As we propose it, patients living in the community would be the responsibility of the same staff responsible for in-patient care, and residential, clinical, social work, and training facilities would be provided on a local basis. No distinction need or should be made between hospital and community agencies. Only by this type of service can adequate care be provided for the mentally disordered at all stages in their treatment.

CHAPTER 11

Proposals for the Welfare Services

THE relationship of the Ministry of Health to the democratically elected local health authorities is a delicate and sensitive one. The Ministry has been criticized for placing too much reliance on the initiative of local authorities and has certainly been too tactful and cautious in pursuing minimum standards of care. With the existing administrative structure, however, it is difficult to castigate the Minister of Health and persuade him to take up a more intrepid attitude in his dealings with backward local authorities, even though there is some evidence that medical officers of health, for example, would welcome more policy guidance on standards of provision.

Most large organizations have problems in co-ordinating their efforts to produce the best possible results. It is usually necessary in industry as well as in the public services for administrators to issue memoranda and directives stressing the need for greater consultation, co-operation, and communication. This is obviously of particular importance for an organization employing over half a million people and with a budget in the order of £1600 million per annum. It becomes crucial when this organization is concerned with the health and welfare of virtually every member of the community.

The Ministry of Health stresses that co-operation is actively sought and that circulars are issued to help remedy defective integration. But with the health service split into three, with three authorities, three employers, three sets of administrative traditions, and three interpretations of Ministry circulars—such exhortations inevitably achieve less than might be possible if the basic structure of the service were changed.

The basic problems of the local health and welfare services are undoubtedly staff shortages, inadequate facilities, reliance on untrained staff, as well as increasing responsibilities and the demands of a growing dependant population. Not surprisingly, therefore, the emphasis in the last few years has been on replenishing the health and welfare services and the need to do this was clearly urgent. Until 1959 the level of capital expenditure on the local health and welfare services remained around £5 million per annum. After this date there was a decided increase, stimulated by the preparation and publication of the 10-year estimates contained in the health and welfare plans, the first of which was published in 1963.[1] However, in addition to the need to modernize, rebuild, and improve local authority welfare and social services, there has been continuous and insistent pressure for the reform of the structure of the social services, preferably under one authority. This is not to argue that an integrated structure would eliminate the need for circulars, exhortations, and progress chasing; but it would be an important step towards organizing the service more satisfactorily and more efficiently for the patients and staff and help to make it more responsive to the needs of its users.

The social services provided by local authorities perform several functions, but it is not always obvious which function of the service is to be pre-eminent. The situation is further complicated by the fact that since many local authorities do not have very clear ideas on the objectives of their social services, they do not give any clear policy guidance to their officials and employees. Thus it is possible for the treasurer of a local authority to comment to a children's committee that it is "cheaper for the ratepayers for the children to be committed to an approved school than to be in care on fit person orders". Different sections of the local authority, as this quotation shows only too clearly, have different priorities for action and expenditure, and this produces much confusion and variation in services between local authorities, depending on which departments in each authority have most power to influence policy. The most important factors determining variations do not usually result from rational planning but from the individual authority's past performance, local pressures in the area and the political ideology of the authority. It is this unevenness in the distribution and quality of services which so often leads to disappointment, frustration and a great deal of avoidable human discomfort and unhappiness.

The complexity of local authority decision-making will often affect the type of provision made. Many decisions are not and cannot be generated simply by a concept of one group's need; for example, the decision to embark on a programme of old people's housing might be decided upon mainly to ensure some mobility from existing council houses. The needs of the area might influence policy to some extent but most local authorities do not have adequate facilities to estimate their own demand for services. Estimating demand is made more complex by local authorities' different interpretations of what constitutes need and the inadequacy of most available comparative data. This is clearly illustrated by the wide variations in the definition of a slum produced by different authorities and by variations in the plans for the development of services for the mentally ill, the elderly, and the physically handicapped, as shown in the health and welfare plans. Many local authority services are also limited by what appear to be quite arbitrary restrictions on their supply. Shortages of staff and facilities have already been mentioned, but there are others, such as charges for some services or the use of a means test, or the use of discretionary powers to decide who shall receive a certain service or who shall not.

What is required is to reorganize all sections of the local authority services which are concerned with welfare, and amalgamate them with the other social services, for example child care and probation, under a single authority. The welfare services involved are basically those which aim to provide for mothers and young children, the old, the handicapped, the mentally ill and the homeless. In this way a unified policy could be established and all methods of assistance, consultative or financial, could be reviewed with the aim of achieving simplicity and equality.

The public could then be assured that, no matter where they happen to live, the same facilities would be available, at least so long as adequate personnel could be found to staff the services.

The need for the reorganization of the social work services seems to have been accepted and even welcomed in advance of the publication of the deliberations of the Seebohm Committee, set up by the Government to report on Local Authority and Allied Personal Social Services. In evidence to this committee many of the associations and professions involved in these services have published their ideas for the reorganization of social work.

The most serious drawbacks to the existing local authority reorganization of social work, which have prompted many people to argue for the reform of the social services are listed briefly below.

1. The division of responsibility for social work services among different departments at local authority level.
2. The division of responsibility for social work services among different Ministries at central government level.
3. The failure of the existing system to use the scarce resources of manpower and finance sensibly.
4. The absence of any clear responsibility to make a rational assessment of the deployment and effectiveness of resources.
5. The fragmentation of the present structure which means that the career structure and prospects of promotion for social workers are totally unsatisfactory. This in turn leads to difficulties in recruitment and training, particularly in the recruitment and training of men.
6. The failure of these services in providing a framework within which the needs of the community concerned could be assessed.
7. The overlapping among existing services, as a result of which the needs of the users are not being adequately met.
8. The difficulty in assessing the reactions of the consumer (i.e. the client) to these services.
9. The problems of the limitations of statutory powers which result in failure to provide services for all those who are found to be in need of help.

10. The existence of inter-departmental rivalries, which seriously impedes the development of co-operation and co-ordination.

It is clear that vast problems of co-ordination and co-operation are inherent in the existing system. At present even services within the same authority frequently operate against each other. Inconsistent treatment by different departments in the same local authority causes people to suffer bewilderment and unnecessary distress. The most frequently cited complaint is that of housing departments evicting families without consulting the children's department or the welfare department before the situation becomes irrevocable. A family in consequence is split up at great cost to the community, in terms of finance, and to the individuals involved.

The Association of Child Care Officers in its evidence to Seebohm gave an example of the kind of confusion caused to a family if a mother became an in-patient in a mental home and listed the social work and linked services which could become involved under the present structure. Any or all of the following might become involved—the mental welfare officer, G.P., home help, educational welfare officer, health visitor, child care officer, supplementary benefits officer, housing officer, and, perhaps, a probation officer. They did not mention psychiatric social workers or medical social workers, but their intervention also is certainly not impossible. Integration will not cure all the evils produced by overlapping and duplication, but by organizing so that scarce trained workers are used efficiently, a great deal can be achieved.

A new department of social services should be formed, designed to bring together effectively within one administrative structure all social workers employed by one local authority. As Professor Titmuss has pointed out, the emphasis should be not on any biological or sociological criteria like the family, or fragments of need like mental health or rehabilitation, but on the *service* that is provided to the community.[2] If the reorganization of the social service is restricted merely to providing a so-called "family service", it will immediately fail in one of its most important aims, which is surely to attract those who most need its help and skills. The middle-aged or elderly spinster, the disturbed adolescent living alone, and the unmarried mother will not be inclined to seek the help of a service if so labelled and if so obviously child oriented. The most important aim is to achieve a better standard of care for the users of the services involved. If this remains the guide to reorganization, and if the integration of different types of social workers can be achieved with an acceptable career structure, a great deal will have been accomplished.

The borderline between health and welfare is rarely a firm one, particularly in respect of the social work needs of the elderly, the mentally ill, the unmarried mother, the physically handicapped, and the chronic sick. Even in the fields of child care and probation, the mental and physical health of at least some members of the family is often an important factor. It would be quite feasible therefore to incorporate all the present local authority social work departments under one authority and make this a section of the area health board (A.H.B.), thus combining the welfare functions of the local authority with child care and even with the probation service. The evidence of the Home Office to the Seebohm Committee suggests that the child care service at least could be integrated with the health and welfare services.[3]

In an earlier chapter we propose the merging of the Ministries of Health and Social Security into a new Ministry of Social Affairs, which would also take in the local authority welfare section and the children's department of the Home Office. Overall responsibility would be vested in a Secretary of State for Social Affairs (see Fig. 3). The situation whereby a Cabinet Minister has overall responsibility, but without departmental backing, is wholly unsatisfactory. To achieve the degree of local and central integration that a unified health service involves will necessitate a powerful Minister capable of persuading numerous pressure groups and vested local interests.

It should obviously be the Ministry's role to define standards with the explicit statement of statutory minima. This does not, of course, give any guarantee that such standards would be achieved

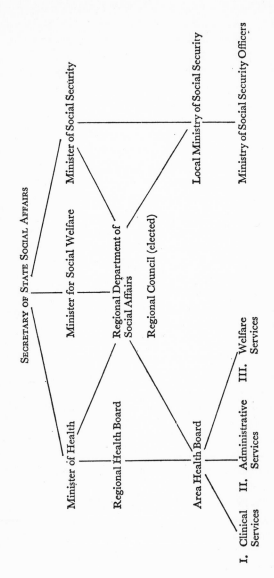

Fig. 3. Diagram of the Structure of the Proposed Ministry of Social Affairs.

with any speed, but it could act as a guide for the regional health board in the distribution of resources and in its programmes of expenditure and recruitment—just as the figures for a maximum of 40 in a primary school class and 30 in a secondary school class help to measure progress towards this standard. An equally important part of the Ministry's role would be deliberately to encourage the raising of standards by the use of liaison officers.

There would obviously be many problems in the formation of an integrated social service unit under the A.H.B. Welfare services have, however, been amalgamated with the health departments for some years now in a large number of local authorities, without becoming submerged by purely medical interests. No doubt, however, the child care and probation services might fear that they would not be given an equal footing with the medical services in the arrangement we propose. We have dealt with this problem by suggesting that the welfare service would be organized under its own manager at A.H.B. level, and that this manager would have right of access to the Minister of Social Welfare. This Minister would also have overall responsibility for all social work, training and recruitment. It would be hoped that gradually a much closer relationship between social workers and Ministry of Social Security officials would develop.

The new department of social service could, theoretically, be administered quite separately from the health service. There are no doubt many who would argue that to leave the social work services under a Ministry which also contains the Ministry of Health would not lead to the most desirable allocation of priorities, and that a more social work oriented department might be more suitable. However, it is difficult to envisage how medical social work, for example, could be organized from a department separate from the health service.

Whether the social service department is organized as a branch of the health service or separately, it will obviously be essential to provide social workers with premises within hospitals and health centres or community care units. Not all social work activities could be operated from these bases, and, indeed, to do so might alienate some clients who might object to being classified, apparently, as "sick", when they intended to ask merely for some financial assistance. Integrated social work centres should be provided for each district. The current use of separate premises, often some distance apart, is wasteful and presents difficulties for both clients and staff. The lack of a focal point in the community to which people in need can apply for help and advice has been repeatedly illustrated in evidence to the Seebohm Committee and in innumerable contributions to social work journals. A unified structure will not necessarily provide the "one door" service which would cope with this barrier, but unified administration would make it possible for there to be a centrally available information service which could direct people to the department and address they need without further referral on their arrival. The evidence of the Institute of Municipal Treasurers and Accountants[4] to Seebohm stresses the need for a central registry service so that better co-ordination can be achieved. It would not, for example, be necessary for a housing authority to employ a housing welfare officer, if information about arrears were centrally available so that preventative action could be taken before the decision to evict and disperse a family became necessary.

Whatever solution is adopted will inevitably involve some kind of compromise. However, if the social services are reorganized at central government level so that there is a more realistic system of administration, planning and research, issues of departmental rivalry would be less important in reorganizing services. Central planning of social work resources would help to provide all social workers with the same kind of ancillary help, and with central record-keeping and secretarial provision, "productivity" might well show a considerable increase as a result. New capital equipment would be required just as urgently with a reorganized administrative structure, but it could be planned to take account of the needs of the whole community, not simply based on the needs of a segment of the service or on those services which must be provided by statute.

CHAPTER 12

Wales—A Pilot Study

THE council of the British Medical Association in 1965 passed a recommendation: "That the Principality of Wales be accepted as a most suitable area in which to conduct a pilot scheme for area health boards." In 1967 the Government published firm proposals for local government reform involving the establishment of eight major local authorities in the Principality. [1] The Government has made it clear that it considers that these recommendations will be implemented in isolation from any recommendations of the Royal Commissions studying the reform of local government in England and Scotland. It seems therefore particularly relevant to formulate concrete proposals for a pilot scheme based on Wales. This would help to avoid some of the teething problems that a major change throughout the country would inevitably bring and help towards the achievement of an agreed scheme.

At present in Wales the hospital services are administered by the Welsh Hospital Board and eighteen hospital management committees, with the teaching hospitals managed by the Board of Governors of the United Cardiff Hospitals. The health and welfare services are provided by 13 county councils, 4 county borough councils, and 1 municipal borough council exercising delegated powers. The G.P., dental, ophthalmic, and pharmaceutical services are provided through contracts with fifteen executive councils.

The new proposals for local government in Wales suggest the formation of only 8 major units, 5 county councils and 3 county borough councils. We recommend that there be 1 Welsh Regional

Health Board (R.H.B.) and 8 Area Health Boards (A.H.B.s), and that these A.H.B.s have the same catchment area as is represented by the 8 major local authorities. It is realized that this involves the abolition of the Board of Governors of the United Cardiff Hospitals, and this will certainly be a controversial recommendation. The Welsh National School of Medicine would, of course, retain its separate identity under the University of Wales and the U.G.C., but the day-to-day running of the teaching hospitals would be integrated with the other hospitals in the Cardiff area and the general-practitioner and local authority health and welfare services.

It is felt that the separation of teaching hospitals cannot continue if the concept of community care is to be fostered at the most formative stage of a doctor's training. The teaching hospitals in this case would form the major proportion of the Cardiff A.H.B.'s hospital services, and it would be inconceivable that the administration of the A.H.B. would not be fully conscious of the special nature of the requirements of a teaching hospital. It is now accepted that teaching hospitals should act as district general hospitals, and the trend of modern medicine is away from the isolated concept of a teaching hospital serving only the specialist requirements of the region. It would be impossible to create a special A.H.B. for the teaching hospital, as this would leave a complex of hospitals for the rest of Cardiff that would not form a viable unit. The teaching hospital would retain its privilege of direct access to the Welsh Board of Health, since we have recommended that this be granted to all A.H.B.s. It might be reasonable for the Ministry to make an arrangement whereby those boards which contained within them a teaching hospital should deal with officers specializing in this particular field, and their budget would obviously be adjusted to make allowance for their added functions regarding teaching and research. But there is no reason to believe that "their role as salients in medical advance" [2] would be prejudiced. There is anyhow in Cardiff a tradition of integration, and teaching hospitals are nowhere near as remote from the community as some of the London teaching hospitals.

We have hesitated before discussing detailed arrangements for Wales, realizing that our own knowledge is inadequate and fearing that people will tend to dismiss the general ideas behind integration because of some anomalies in detail. Provided these suggestions are taken only as an outline we believe they might help to indicate how A.H.B.s could work on the ground. We also include as an appendix rather more comprehensive details of the distribution of existing health resources in Wales so that they can serve as a reference point for anyone interested.

As a detailed example the proposed new Welsh Authority of Gwynedd is taken (see Appendix I for details). Ideally this new and enlarged local authority unit should be linked with the same geographical boundaries as the A.H.B. The population of the area (at present five counties) was 553,460 in June 1966. As part of the 10-year hospital plan the Welsh Hospital Board plans to establish a district general hospital at Bangor to serve the whole of Anglesey, Caernarvonshire, and part of Merioneth (population of 189,540)* and one at Rhyl to serve parts of Denbighshire and Flintshire (population of 162,987)† the remainder being served by Wrexham D.G.H. Because of their definition of catchment areas the population from four existing rural and urban councils in Merioneth (totalling 16,000) are to be served by the district general hospital at Aberystwyth—which does not come within the proposed new authority of Gwynedd. Nevertheless, this does show two district general hospitals under the purview of one A.H.B., and also in this area there are at present five local health authorities. Our proposals involve transferring local health authority functions to the A.H.B., perhaps acting through the district general hospital locally. Thus the hospital at Bangor could provide the administrative centre for local health services in Anglesey and Caernarvonshire with perhaps Merioneth; and the hospital at Rhyl likewise for the present areas of Denbighshire C.C., Colwyn Bay, Denbigh M.B., Ruthin M.B., Flintshire C.C., and Flint M.B. In addition the A.H.B. would also have within its area the psychiatric hospital at Denbigh and the hospitals for the mentally

* 193,038 by 1981.   † 164,899 by 1981.

sub-normal, and a suitable number of community care units or health centres.

Under the proposals for reorganizing local government in Wales, 5 new administrative counties replace 13 existing and 1 county borough, and 36 new district councils replace 164 other local districts. In addition 3 county boroughs remain. If the health services were likewise reorganized to coincide with local government boundaries, there would be a consequent reduction of hospital groups from 18 to 8 A.H.B.s.

The proposals of the Welsh Hospital Board for the establishment of district general hospitals as part of their 1962 10-year plan have drawn slightly different catchment areas to that of the Welsh Office, when constructing their proposals for local government reform in 1967, so this does not enable a detailed model for the Principality to be constructed from the information at our disposal. However, the details given for Gwynedd do provide a field-work example of the size, scope and complexity of services under the purview of one A.H.B.

A further example, this time of an urban community, is provided by the Cardiff area. It is the stated intention to develop acute services for Cardiff around the University Hospital of Wales which will have 800 beds including the dental hospital. Cardiff, as the medical centre for Wales, as well as the civic capital, will in addition be catering for a variety of regional specialties, like plastic surgery, now at Chepstow. The University Hospital of Wales will also contain an acute psychiatric admission unit, but the bulk of Cardiff patients will still have to go to Whitchurch Hospital, which is planned to have 835 beds by 1970, and is not grouped administratively with the teaching hospital. Mental subnormality beds for Cardiff and districts are at present provided at Ely Hospital, now with 471 beds, but with plans for additional beds.

At present the population of Cardiff (259,700 in 1966) is served by the United Cardiff Hospitals, Cardiff Hospital Group, and some hospitals in the former Rhymney and Sirhowy Valleys Group, now administered as the new Cardiff North and District

Group. The local health authority is Cardiff County Borough
Council. At present it provides one health centre, and the
revision of the health and welfare plan to 1976 indicates the
provision of a further 3 by 1971 (some of these could be replanned
as community care units). The number of child welfare and
maternity clinics is to be reduced from 21 to 17 in the same
period. There are no day nurseries provided, and none planned.
An increase from 1 to 2 adult training centres for the mentally
subnormal is envisaged, but the provision for juniors will remain
the same. Two adult hostels and one junior are planned by 1971.

One occupation centre, and an increase from 1 hostel to 4 for
the mentally ill are indicated. Centres and homes for the elderly
will increase from 4 to 17 and from 13 to 23 respectively. The
provision of centres for physically handicapped will increase from
7 to 12, but no home for the physically handicapped will be
provided before 1976. The ratios per thousand of the population
for domiciliary workers will be as follows, the only substantial
increase being in the home help provision:

	1965	1976
Health visitors	from 0·19 to 0·17	
Home helps	from 0·59 to 0·74	
Home nurses	from 0·17 to 0·17	
Midwives	from 0·10 to 0·09	
Social workers	from 0·09 to 0·11	

Between 1966–7 and 1970–1, the authority estimated spending
£1,827,555 on capital building works, and by 1975–6 to have
increased this total by only £226,000 to £2,053,555. Within the
proposed Cardiff local government area there will be fifteen
hospitals, with at present a total of 3,249 beds. As the present
hospital catchment areas and local government boundaries do
not coincide, it is impossible to estimate with accuracy how this
total compares with the Ministry of Health's optimum figures of
3·3 acute beds for 1000 population, of 0·58 maternity beds, of 10

geriatric beds (per 1000 population over 65) of 1·8 mental illness beds, and 1·3 beds for mental subnormality.

The first hospital 10-year plan (1962), which might be held to be the optimistic statement of ideals by hospital boards, showed that by 1975, the university hospital would have grown in size and importance at the expense of ten cottage and small hospitals (770 beds in all) but still giving a total of 3380 beds. Subsequent amendments to the plan, in the light of realistic stringency by the Ministry, has made comparison impossible.

From this it would appear that the university hospital is going to undertake district general hospital functions for the Cardiff population, and the beds in the Cardiff group will presumably decline in importance, or simply complement the university hospital services in some way. It should be noted that the teaching group at present administers Llandough Hospital (383 beds) at Penarth. In order to obtain maximum efficiency and inter-availability, the hospitals clearly ought to be under one administrative control. The Cardiff A.H.B. offers such a facility.

A different scheme based on *ad hoc* health areas for Wales has been suggested in a report prepared by a subcommittee of the Welsh B.M.A. Committee which proposes 6 or 7 A.H.B.s for Wales.[3] Given this readiness amongst the medical profession to integrate the Health services in Wales it should be possible to introduce an agreed scheme within even a few years.

Tables of Statistics

Annexe 1. Population and areas of the proposed new counties, county boroughs, and districts and their component units

(A) *Counties*

New administrative county	Population*	Area (acres)	Present administrative areas covered by new authority
Gwynedd	553,460	1,554,858	The counties of Anglesey, Caernarvonshire, Merioneth, Denbighshire, and Flintshire
Powys	116,470	1,280,556	The counties of Montgomeryshire, Radnorshire and Breconshire
Dyfed	316,640†	1 428,851†	The counties of Cardiganshire, Pembrokeshire and Carmarthenshire (except for a small part of Llandeilo Rural District) together with a very small part of Pontardawe Rural District and Llwchwr Urban District
Glamorgan	721,820†	441,989†	The existing county (except for most of Caerphilly and Gelligaer Urban Districts and small parts of Llwchwr Urban District and Cardiff and Pontardawe Rural Districts) together with most of Merthyr Tydfil County Borough and a small part of Llandeilo Rural District
Gwent	419,900†	371,280†	The county of Monmouthshire together with most of Caerphilly and Gelligaer Urban Districts and a small part of Merthyr Tydfil County Borough and Cardiff Rural District

(B) *County Boroughs*

New county borough	Population*	Area (acres)	Present administrative areas covered by new authority
Cardiff	289,050†	19,755†	The existing county borough
Swansea	170,870†	21,632†	The existing county borough subject to the changes recommended by the local government commission
Newport	113,000	11,185†	The existing county borough

* Based on Registrar General's estimate, 30 June, 1966.
† Approximations.

ANNEXE 2.[1] ESTIMATED NUMBER OF GENERAL PRACTITIONERS AND DENTISTS (INCLUDING ASSISTANTS) PREDOMINANTLY PRACTISING IN THE NEW COUNTY AND COUNTY BOROUGH AREAS DEFINED IN CMD. 3340

Area	General practitioners*	Dentists (including assistants)
Gwynedd	271	87
Powys	63	19
Dyfed	162	52
Glamorgan	324	90
Gwent and Newport†	202	65
Cardiff	135	72
Swansea	82	32

* There are, of course, many cases where general practitioners and dentists, especially those living on the borders of counties, operate in more than one area. General Practitioners have therefore been shown under the area in which they have the greatest number of patients and dentists under the area in which they are resident.

† In the case of Gwent and Newport C.B.C., however, combined figures are given as the Monmouthshire and Newport C.B.C. areas are at present covered by one executive council and it would be a substantial task to give separate figures.

[1] We are grateful to the Welsh Hospital Board, Welsh Board of Health, and the Welsh Office for allowing us to publish annexes 2, 3, and 4 which they kindly prepared.

ANNEXE 3. HOSPITALS WITHIN THE NEW COUNTIES AND COUNTY BOROUGHS OF WALES

Key to Class of Hospital

A	Acute	MI	Mental Illness
C	Chronic	ML	Mainly Long-stay
C(A)	Children's Acute	MS	Mentally Subnormal
Con.	Convalescent	O	Other hospitals
G	Gynaecology	Ophth.	Ophthalmic
Ger.	Geriatrics	Orth.	Orthopaedic
I	Isolation	P	Pre-convalescent
L	Long stay	PA	Partly Acute
M	Maternity	PS	Plastic Surgery
MA	Mainly Acute	TC	Tuberculosis and Chest
MC	Maladjusted Children	TCI	Tuberculosis, Chest and Isolation

GWYNEDD

Hospital	Location		Beds	Class
Towyn and District War Memorial	Towyn		20	A
Oakwood Park	Conway		201	MS
Caernarvonshire and Anglesey General	Bangor		174	A
St. David's	Bangor		164	MC
Minffordd	Bangor		40	C(A)
Groesynyd	Conway		36	P
Llandudno General	Llandudno		138	A
Llandudno Maternity	Llandudno		6	M
Stanley Sailors	Holyhead		27	A
Gors Maternity	Holyhead		17	M
Valley	Valley		53	C
Druid	Llangefni		46	Ger.
Caernarvon Eye and Cottage	Caernarvon		29	Ophth.
Eryri	Caernarvon		90	MA
Galltysil	Caernarvon		50	C/I
Ffestiniog Memorial	Blaenau Ffestiniog		16	A
Madoc Memorial	Portmadoc		12	A
Bryn Beryl	Pwllheli		27	A
Conway	Nr. Conway:	Hospital	67	C
		Part III	54	
Pwllheli	Pwllheli:	Hospital	43	C
		Part III	26	
Cefni	Llangefni		31	Ger.
Brynseiont Sanatorium	Caernarvon		36	TC

Hospital	Location		Beds	Class
Bronygarth	Penrhyndeudraeth		58	C
North Wales	Denbigh		1,200	MI
Pool Park	Ruthin		—	MI
"Gwynfa"	Upper Colwyn Bay		25	MC
Colwyn Bay and West Denbigh	Colwyn Bay		60	A
Bronynant Isolation	Colwyn Bay		25	I
Colwyn Bay Maternity Home	Colwyn Bay		16	M
Prince Edward War Memorial	Rhyl		31	Orth.
Royal Alexandra	Rhyl		141	A
H.M. Stanley	St. Asaph		224	MA/M
Denbigh Infirmary	Denbigh		50	A
Ruthin	Ruthin		37	A
Flint Cottage	Flint		26	A
Holywell Cottage	Holywell		23	A
Catherine Gladstone Maternity Home	Mancot		25	M
Chatsworth House Maternity Home	Prestatyn		29	M/Orth.
Lluesty General	Holywell		151	C
Abergele Chest	Abergele		144	ML
Llangwyfan	Denbigh		210	TC
Coed Du Hall	Mold		80	MS
Llwyn View	Dolgellau		68	MS
Broughton	Nr. Chester		70	MS
Garth Angharad	Dolgellau		74	MS
Maelor General	Wrexham:	Hospital	571	MA
		Part III	37	
Wrexham and East Denbighshire War Memorial	Wrexham		203	A
Chirk and District	Chirk		34	A
Llangollen Cottage	Llangollen		20	A
Mold	Mold		21	A
Trevalyn Manor	Rossett		55	C
Dolgellau and District	Dolgellau		17	A
Barmouth Maternity Home	Barmouth		6	M
Meadowslea	Penyffordd		75	C
Hawarden	Buckley		68	C
Polish Hospital	Penley		113	C

POWYS

Hospital	Location	Beds	Class
Crickhowell War Memorial	Crickhowell	25	A
Breconshire War Memorial	Brecon	40	A
St. David's	Brecon	46	C
Llandrindod Wells War Memorial	Llandrindod Wells	43	A
Builth Cottage	Builth Wells	25	A
Knighton	Knighton	32	C
South Wales Sanatorium	Talgarth	233	TC
Adelina Patti	Swansea Valley	93	C
Machynlleth and District	Machynlleth	16	A
Llanidloes and District	Llanidloes	56	ML
Montgomery County Infirmary	Newtown	30	A
Machynlleth Chest	Machynlleth	35	TC
Mid Wales	Talgarth	528	MI
Brynhyfryd	Forden	195	MS/C
Llys Maldwyn	Caersws	150	MS
Victoria Memorial	Welshpool	23	A

DYFED

Hospital	Location	Beds	Class
Amman Valley	Glanamman	53	A
Llanelli	Llanelli	152	A
Bryntirion	Llanelli	150	L
Glasfryn Maternity	Llanelli	12	M
Cilymaenllwyd	Llanelli	43	P
West Wales General: (a) Priory Street (b) Glangwili	Carmarthen	313	A
Pembroke County War Memorial: (a) Haverfordwest (b) Withybush	Haverfordwest	163	A
South Pembrokeshire	Pembroke Dock	83	PA
Cardigan and District Memorial	Cardigan	36	A
Llandovery Cottage	Llandovery	18	A
Tenby Cottage	Tenby	16	A

Hospital	Location	Beds	Class
Kensington	St. Brides, Haverfordwest	60	TC
St. Thomas	Haverfordwest	92	ML
West Wales Chest Hospital	Llanybyther	52	TC
West Wales Isolation	Tumble	58	ML
St. David's	Carmarthen	1,000	MI
Pantglas Hall	Llanfynydd	124	MS
Bronglais General	Aberystwyth	274	A
Aberayron Cottage	Aberayron	14	A
Tregaron	Tregaron	32	L

GLAMORGAN

Hospital	Location	Beds	Class
Prince of Wales Orthopaedic	Rhydlafar	270	Orth.
Barry Accident and Surgical	Barry	45	A
Barry Neale–Kent	Barry	30	C
Barry Maternity	Barry	27	M
Sully	Sully	318	O
St. Mary's	Penarth	38	C
Merthyr General	Merthyr	116	A
St. Tydfil's	Merthyr	265	MA
Gwaunfarren	Merthyr	30	M
Mardy Isolation	Merthyr	112	PA
Mountain Ash General	Mountain Ash	51	A
Aberdare General	Aberdare	102	A
Lady Aberdare Maternity	Mountain Ash	15	M
Fedw Hir	Aberdare	40	C
Pontypridd and District	Pontypridd	36	A
Dewi Sant	Pontypridd: Hospital Part III	123 41	ML
East Glamorgan General	Church Village	330	A
Tonteg	Tonteg	55	ML
Rhiwfelin	Llantrisant	28	C
Llwynypia	Llwynypia	195	A
Porth and District	Porth	94	PA
Tyntyla	Ystrad	118	L
Pentwyn Cottage	Treorchy	24	A
Treherbert	Treherbert	34	A
Penrhys Smallpox	Rhondda	14	I

Hospital	Location	Beds	Class
Glyncornel	Llwynypia	52	ML
Bridgend and District	Bridgend	36	O
Bridgend General	Bridgend	408	MA
Cefn Hirgoed	Cefn Hirgoed	78	ML
Heddfan	Cefn Hirgoed	16	C
Maesteg General	Maesteg	67	A
Maesteg Isolation	Maesteg	18	P/I
Llwydarth	Maesteg	13	A
Blackmill Isolation	Blackmill	44	P/I
Neath General	Neath	412	A
Port Talbot and District	Port Talbot	85	A
Groeswen	Port Talbot	58	PA
Tonna Children's	Nr. Neath	84	C(A)
Cymla Chest	Neath	77	L
Maesgwyn	Bryncethin	61	C
Stouthall	Reynoldston	33	P
Gorseinon	Gorseinon	71	A
Garngoch	Gorseinon	38	TC
Clydach War Memorial	Nr. Swansea	26	MA
Gellinudd	Pontardawe	33	L
Morgannwg (comprising Glanrhyd, Penyfai and Parc Hospitals)	Bridgend	2,027	MI
Hensol Castle	Pontyclun	771	MS
Drymma Hall	Skewen	84	MS
Talygarn Miners' Rehabilitation Centre	Talygarn	106	O
Llandough	Penarth	383	A
Fairwood Maternity	Swansea	16	M

GWENT

Hospital	Location	Beds	Class
Pontypool and District	Pontypool	118	A
Cefn Illa Maternity	Nr. Usk	22	M
County	Griffithstown	282	MA
Snatchwood House	Pontnewynydd, Nr. Pontypool	30	P
Chepstow and District	Chepstow	21	A
Cefn Mably	St. Mellons, Nr. Cardiff	146	TC

Hospital	Location	Beds	Class
Mount Pleasant	Chepstow	260	L
St. Lawrence	Chepstow	201	PS/Orth.
Oakdale	Blackwood	14	C
St. Cadoc's	Caerleon	504	MI
Llanfrechfa Grange	Cwmbran	524	MS
Monmouth General	Monmouth	26	A
Victoria Cottage	Abergavenny	40	A
Blaenavon Workmen's	Blaenavon	25	MA
Blaina and District	Nantyglo	44	A
Ebbw Vale	Ebbw Vale	86	A
Abertillery and District	Aberbeeg	44	A
Nevill Hall	Abergavenny	44	A
Tredegar General	Tredegar	40	Ger.
St. James	Tredegar	132	A
Pen-y-Val	Abergavenny	1,055	MI
Maindiff Court	Abergavenny	120	MI
Abertysswg Workmen's	Abertysswg	12	A
Redwood Memorial	Rhymney	20	A
Aberbargoed and District	Aberbargoed	32	A
Bedwellty Isolation	Aberbargoed	24	C
Caerphilly District Miners	Caerphilly	192	A
Van Annexe, Caerphilly	Caerphilly	25	—
Energlyn	Caerphilly	64	ML
Gelligaer	Hengoed	51	TCI
Ystrad Mynach	Ystrad Mynach	72	Ger.

CARDIFF C.B.C.

Hospital	Location	Beds	Class
St. David's	Cardiff	481	MA
Prince of Wales Orthopaedic (Out-patients only)	Cardiff	—	Orth.
Royal Hamadryad General and Seamen's	Cardiff	66	O
Lansdowne	Cardiff	170	MA
Caerau	Cyntwell, Cardiff	54	C
Children's E.N.T.	Ely	56	O
Glan Ely	Fairwater	214	ML
Rookwood	Llandaff	212	A
Whitchurch	Cardiff	729	MI

Hospital	Location	Beds	Class
Ely	Cardiff	612	MS/MI
Velindre	Cardiff	100	O
Cardiff Royal Infirmary (including William Nicholls Convalescent Home)	Cardiff	418	A
Cardiff Maternity	Cardiff	118	M
Lord Pontypridd	Cardiff	19	O
University of Wales Dental Hospital (Out-patients only)	Cardiff	—	O

SWANSEA C.B.C.

Hospital	Location	Beds	Class
Swansea	Swansea	412	A
Singleton	Swansea	—	O/P only
Mount Pleasant	Swansea: Hospital Part III	226 34	ML
Hill House	Swansea	120	TCI
Cefn Coed	Cockett, Swansea	666	MI
Westfa Hospital Day Centre	116 Eaton Crescent, Swansea	—	MI
Llwyneryr	Swansea	27	MS
Morriston	Morriston	510	A

NEWPORT C.B.C.

Hospital	Location	Beds	Class
Royal Gwent	Newport	428	A
St. Woolos	Newport: Hospital Part III	274 28	MA
Allt-yr-Yn Isolation	Newport	104	I/P
Lydia Beynon Maternity	Newport	27	M

ANNEXE 4. WELSH HOSPITAL BOARD. PROPOSED HOSPITAL
DEVELOPMENT—WALES

Estimated Population as at 30 June, 1966; Projected Population
1971; and Projected Population 1981 for each Proposed District
General Hospital Area
Projections Amended April, 1966

Summary

District general hospital area	Estimated population as at 30.6.66	Projected population 1971	+ or − 1966 to 1971	Projected population 1981	+ or − 1966 to 1981
Newport	196,727	204,398	+7,671	212,873	+25,146
West Monmouthshire	149,306	156,322	+7,016	169,128	+19,822
Abergavenny	121,240	125,749	+4,509	133,318	+12,078
Cardiff	453,774	480,705	+26,931	525,493	+71,719
Merthyr	171,948	182,319	+10,371	192,478	+20,530
East Glamorgan	179,761	187,338	+7,577	197,235	+17,474
Bridgend	125,464	129,022	+3,558	139,273	+13,809
Neath	132,370	140,688	+8,318	151,031	+18,661
Swansea	337,250	348,305	+11,055	361,722	+24,472
Carmarthen	191,440	193,448	+2,008	202,077	+10,637
Aberystwyth	87,810	87,550	−260	88,767	+957
Bangor	189,540	188,387	−1,153	193,038	+3,498
Rhyl	162,987	158,075	− 4,912	164,899	+1,912
Wrexham	201,593	205,332	+3,739	216,375	+14,782
TOTALS	2,701,210	2,787,638	+86,428	2,956,707	+255,497

Case-histories*

Mrs. "A" ————

Example of difficulties for a family resulting from:

    (A)   Serious chronic illness.
    (B)   Lack of liaison between hospital and local welfare services and the G.P.
    (C)   Medical responsibility in the hands of a humane and efficient G.P. but one who is nevertheless inadequately briefed in the handling of this situation, and who is unable to give the necessary support to the family.

Mrs. A, aged 31, suffers from a chronic deteriorating disease of the central nervous sytem diagnosed in 1964, although the symptoms had occurred earlier soon after the birth of her daughter who is now aged 6. Her husband describes her as "being afflicted with a constant tremor and agitation and her mental condition is one of almost complete dementure. She can feed herself and dress very slowly (about 1–2 hours): she is becoming increasingly difficult to deal with, having no will to do anything, in a constant state of indecision even over trifles, shows negativism and there is increasing aphasia which renders her almost incoherent." Mr. A says that his wife cannot be left alone for long. She has fallen downstairs more than once, and even after a fairly slight fall tends to be completely helpless. He dares not leave their child with her alone for long as it is dangerous for both.

Mrs. A has received either out-patient or in-patient treatment at five hospitals: at only one of these did Mr. A feel that he received any sympathetic understanding or guidance from a doctor. He writes: "at the hospitals, with one exception, the procedure was for the doctors to say very little to me and add that they were sending a report to my medical practitioner. The one exception was when I had a long conversation with one doctor who seemed to know much more about the illness. Perhaps I am wrong but most G.P.s seem to know little of psychiatric illness. They told me no treatment was possible because the trouble is genetic, and nothing can be done with a defective gene which is dominant. I have never at any place been referred to a medical social worker."

* We are grateful to the Disablement Income Group, Rellen House, Godalming, Surrey, for their kindness in making available these case-histories which have been investigated by their own trained social worker.

Yet Mr. A continues: "let me say that I have the greatest admiration for the work of doctors and hospital staff. Until my wife's illness I had hardly seen a hospital or doctor, but since then I have seen a good deal. In hospitals in particular they are grossly overworked and so are doctors, but the system is wrong. G.P.s now simply diagnose or write a prescription. Anything else or, if they are not sure, they send to a hospital. I have been appalled by the great numbers of people waiting in hospital for hours then seeing a doctor for two or three minutes—perhaps just to have a dressing changed, or to take a specimen for analysis and so on. Quite obviously in between G.P. and the hospital there should be a medical centre where all the more trivial complaints can be attended to. My own experiences are these. In the first place the doctors were reluctant to name the condition from which my wife suffers because as one told me it is the equivalent of a death sentence. Then I was told nothing whatever could be done and the only solution was a home. Apparently I am regarded as a fool because I keep her at home. Doctors cannot help me because if I keep my wife at home my troubles are on my own head. I asked the doctor if a health visitor could call. He said there was no real provision for this, only the district nurse. She called twice then stopped, but she is only used to visiting pregnant mothers and knows nothing of mental illness. I tried again and another official arrived, a very nice man who deals with disabled persons. He suggested that my wife go to a basket-making class or take up remedial swimming; both suggestions were so ludicrous that I asked him if he knew what my wife was suffering from—he did not. I said could someone call once a week and talk to my wife for an hour or take her for a ride in the car. He said he had no facilities of that nature and I haven't seen him since. All my contacts have been of this nature. People call once, make some suggestion which is impracticable and then disappear permanently. The problem is simple as far as I see it. There is simply no organization or body of people trained and with the knowledge to deal with mentally sick people. The State as far as I can discover makes no provision for mental illness outside of institutions and hospitals. But please let me repeat, I imply no criticism of doctors, officials or voluntary bodies, all of whom I believe do an excellent job amid great difficulties."

Mr. A writes elsewhere: "I have spoken very frankly with my G.P. for whom I have a high regard. He can do nothing and it is no good in my wife's case saying a few soothing words. His time is much better spent in saving a baby's life or a young person's health who has the chance of a happy useful life. This is the stark brutal truth and I acknowledge it. Doctor——is very busy and at the moment has no partner. He has invariably come when I have asked him. But no one has ever come near her unless I have made a specific request. I find it extremely difficult to get information on how to deal with her. I need a book on mental health nursing. For example, she has fallen downstairs more than once, once seriously. I told the doctor this and he made these suggestions, (a) she should walk downstairs backwards (n.b. she fell downstairs going upwards). I pointed out to him (1) she probably did not understand what he was saying (2) if she did understand, it is unlikely she would remember (3) if she did understand and remember it is unlikely she would have the will to act on his instructions (4) she would fall whichever way she went up and down stairs; (b) his second suggestion was that I should pad all sharp corners in the house with foam rubber. This just seemed impracticable. There are all sorts of other difficulties arising which I am finding it difficult to cope with."

PRACTICAL ARRANGEMENTS

Mr. A has a home help who he describes as satisfactory within her terms of reference. She washes clothes, etc., makes beds and does domestic work at the cost of £2 10s. 0d. a week, for 2 hours, 5 days a week. He has no assistance of any description at weekends or holidays. He has entirely looked after his daughter for the last 3 years: his wife can do nothing. Mr. A says that he buys all the food and prepares all meals and deals with most of the household duties other than that done by the home help. He has tried getting assistance apart from the home help but has found no one suitable which he can afford. The labour exchange sends all sorts of people, some of them only stayed a few days, others leave without notice or are unreliable.

FOR THE FUTURE

Mr. A writes: "all doctors of course say that my wife should be in an institution, but I am reluctant to permit this. She is only 31 and most people in these homes are aged. I cannot really tell how much she experiences pain and pleasure, but she still does to some extent and is not completely insane all the time. I have to take her out, of course, which I do as often as I can, chiefly at weekends. Perhaps it is not necessary for me to say that I rarely if ever go out alone myself and the word holiday is meaningless. Voluntary bodies cannot deal with this situation. Ordinary people simply do not know how to deal with people affected mentally."

Mrs. "B" ————

This material also shows the difficulties for a family resulting from:

(A)   A serious chronic illness.
(B)   The undeveloped nature of local authority services.

Mrs. B is aged 37 and suffers from 3 serious chronic conditions. Mrs. B's husband is a professional person, and she has three school-age children.

Mrs. B describes her difficulties as being those of managing at home, loneliness, and caring for her children.

She has a paid help of 3 hours per week who cleans the kitchen and does the basic cleaning; but who does no spring-cleaning nor does she clean the cooker, windows, curtains, or any non-essential jobs. She describes the local home help service as being useless—without a paid organizer.

The nature of the medical condition is such that there are large quantities of washing and there is no county service for laundry.

Shopping is a difficulty. Mrs. B feels that what would help her would be meals-on-wheels for school holidays, and entertainment for children. Secondly, heavy duty home help. Third, information on what help is available, that is appliances etc.

Mrs. B says she keeps sane by doing voluntary typing at a hospital where she is taken by car once a week.

Mrs. "C" ————

Example of difficulties for a family resulting from:

    (A)   Serious chronic illness.
    (B)   Gaps in local authority services.
    (C)   Lack of social security provision for a disabled housewife.

Mrs. C is in her late 30's, married and with two school-age children. She has had rheumatoid arthritis for about 7 years. Following a spell in hospital, it was felt that she was not fit to go to her own home and she has since lived with her sister, who also has two children of her own. The sister gives tea each day to Mrs. C's children, after which they go home with their father for bed and breakfast. Friends of the family have joined in an informal rota so that Mrs. C's sister has two mornings a week free to shop and Mr. C has a babysitter two evenings a week: other family emergencies such as doctors' visits, school interviews, etc., can also be dealt with through these friends as they arise. The district nurse visits twice daily, one to bath and dress Mrs. C and the evening visit is for a suppository.

The present situation is satisfactory for a short time, but the house is small and the family is anxious to return as a unit to their own home; there is concern for the children's sake as the boy of 11 is presenting difficulties such as lying, stealing and generally disorderly conduct both at home and at school.

The medical social worker at the hospital referred the family to the local authority's welfare department and recently the deputy medical officer of health visited Mr. C with a welfare officer. Unfortunately they seem to have reached a deadlock between them. If Mrs. C returns to her own home, they say they cannot guarantee that any home help can attend at any particular time, although if borough and voluntary help are to co-operate in seeing that she is not left alone for long periods, it is obviously essential that her friends should have some idea when help will be there. The family are not willing that she should be left except for short periods, in view of her condition and inability to move in case of fire, intruders and so on. An electric chair has been ordered through the welfare department and this would help Mrs. C to reach the telephone, bang on a wall, etc. The family's idea of the borough and themselves co-operating with the employment of a full-time help has been turned down by the welfare authorities who say that there are no powers for them to do this.

The welfare authority suggests that Mrs. C should enter a home. The family and her friends both think she is unlikely ever to leave one and if they can manage to keep her at home even for a few years more while the children are still young, it would be well worth while.

Mr. "D" ————

This is an example of difficulties for a family resulting from:

- (A) Chronic mental and physical disablement.
- (B) Undeveloped local welfare services.
- (C) Lack of effective social work service in psychiatric hospital and the dangers of responsibility for the giving of social work help to the family being split between too many agencies.

Mr. D is nearly 50 and is registered as disabled, being "fit for light work only". Living in the north of England, he has found it nearly impossible to find light work through the labour exchange, and in fact has had only 3 weeks work over the past 13 years.

Mr. D has valvular heart disease and this has resulted in a stroke, necessitating in-patient hospital treatment. Three of his children have had periods in care after the family became homeless. Later a council house was found for them.

Mr. D's allowance from the Ministry of Social Security was subject to the wage stop, but on appeal, this has now been lifted.

Mr. D has recently received in-patient treatment in a psychiatric hospital and an attempt to secure for him the help of a psychiatric social worker was in vain because there is no such department in this psychiatric hospital. The children's department is now aware of this family but the problem is clearly seen to spill out over the boundaries of the different welfare agencies. Over the years Mr. D has been known to hospitals and clinics, welfare departments, children's departments, and education departments. The existence of his problems today show how ineffective the help available to him and his family has been.

Mr. "E" ————

Example of lack of facilities in community care for the mentally disabled.

Mr. E has lived in a mental hospital for the past 20 years. The social worker writes that "his mental condition is such that he needs some kind of asylum, and our hospital happens to be the only kind of home at present that will accept him. If there was a hostel for people who need supervision but not medical care, then Mr. E would be suitable for such a hostel. As it is, there are no such places yet that I know of."

References

CHAPTER 1

1. National Health Service Act. 1946, H.M.S.O., London.
2. A. J. WILLCOCKS, *The Creation of the National Health Service*, Routledge and Kegan Paul, Library of Social Policy and Administration.
3. *Report on Social Insurance and Allied Services*, Cmd. 6404, 1942.
4. *A National Health Service*, Cmd. 6502, 1944.
5. *Enquiry into the Cost of the National Health Service*, the Report of the Guillebaud Committee, Cmd. 9663, 1956.
6. *A Review of the Medical Services in Great Britain*, Porritt Committee, 1962.
7. *Local Government in Wales*, Cmd. 3340, 1967.
8. *Hansard*, 24 May 1966, col. 297.

CHAPTER 2

1. *Health Services and Public Health Bill*, H.M.S.O., December 1967.
2. *Social Work and the Community*, Cmd. 3065, 1966.
General References:
   Handbook for Members of Hospital Management Committees, H.M.S.O. for Ministry of Health, 1967.
   The National Health Service, Hill and Woodcock 1949, Johnson.
   Hospitals and the State, Acton Society Survey published as 6 papers 1955–9.
   A. LINDSEY, *Socialized Medicine in England and Wales*, O.U.P., 1962.

CHAPTER 3

This chapter is based on a Young Fabian Pamphlet, *General Practice*, written by two of the authors in July 1965.
1. Professor J. H. F. BROTHERTON, 70th Congress of the Royal Society of Health, 1963.
2. N. R. BUTLER and D. G. BONHAM, *Perinatal Mortality*, First Report of the 1958 Perinatal Mortality Survey, Livingstone 1963.
3. M. S. T. HOBBS, *British Medical Journal*, **4,** 287, 4 November 1967.
4. J. COLLINGS, *Lancet*, 25 March 1950.
5. S. HADFIELD, *British Medical Journal*, 1953.
6. S. TAYLOR, *Good General Practice*, O.U.P., 1954.
7. S. L. MORRISON, M. M. RILEY, *Medical Care*, **1,** (3) 137 (1963); J. A. H. LEE, M. WEATHERALL, P. DRAPER, *Proceedings of the Royal Society of Medicine*, November 1964.

8. J. COLLINS, *Social Casework in General Medical Practice*, Pitman Medical, 1965.
9. *Report on the Field of Work of the Family Doctor*, H.M.S.O., 1963.
10. R. M. ACHESON, D. J. P. BAKER, W. J. H. BUTTERFIELD, *British Medical Journal*, **2,** 1315 (1962).
11. J. J. MCMULLEN, A. BARR, *Journal of the College of General Practitioners*, January 1964.
12. *Hospital Out-patient Services*, Oxford Regional Hospital Board, 1963.
13. *What Do They Really Want?*, Wessex Regional Hospital Board, 1964.
14. FORSYTH and LOGAN, *The Demand for Medical Care*, O.U.P., 1960.
15. A. CARTWRIGHT, R. MARSHALL, *Medical Care*, **3,** (2) 69, April 1965.
16. *British Medical Journal*, 1962.
17. *A Revised Hospital Plan for England and Wales*, Cmd. 1604, H.M.S.O.
18. S. L. MORRISON, M. M. RILEY, *Medical Care*, July 1963.
19. D. L. CROMBIE, K. W. CROSS, *Medical Care*, 1963.
20. D. BAIRD. Paper given at Royal Society of Health Congress, 1965.
21. T. FOX, *Lancet*, April 1960.
22. J. M. AKESTER, A. W. MACPHAIL, *Lancet*, August 1964.
23. *Family Needs and the Social Services*, P.E.P., 1961.

CHAPTER 4

1. *The Guardian*, 29 July 1967, Letter from Dr. P. H. Shorterhouse.
2. *Report of the Committee on Maladjusted Children*, H.M.S.O., 1955.
3. Association of Education Committees Executive 1959, Minute No. 332.
4. *The Development of Community Care, Health and Welfare*, 1963. Cmd. 1973.
5. *The Development of Community Care, Health and Welfare*, 1966. Cmd. 3022.
6. *Ministry of Health Written Evidence to Royal Commission on Local Government*, H.M.S.O., 1967.
7. Mental Health Act, 1959, H.M.S.O.
8. G. F. REHIN, F. M. MARTIN, *Psychiatric Services in 1975*. P.E.P. Research Services, **xxix,** No. 468, 1963.
9. N. R. BUTLER and D. G. BONHAM, *Perinatal Mortality*, First Report of the 1958 Perinatal Mortality Survey, Livingstone, 1963
10. *The Guardian*, 14 December 1967.

CHAPTER 5

1. N. O'CONNOR and J. TIZARD, *The Social Problem of Mental Deficiency* Pergamon Press, 1956.
2. A. M. CLARKE and A. D. B. CLARKE, *Mental Deficiency—the Changing Outlook*, Methuen, 1961.
3. G. W. BROWN and J. K. WING, A comparative clinical and social survey of three mental hospitals, the Sociological Review Monogr. 5, *Sociology and Medicine*, ed. P. Halmos and Keele, 1962.

4. G. W. BROWN, Experiences of discharged chronic schizophrenic patients in various types of living group, *Millbank Mem. Fund Quarterly*, **37,** 105 (1959).

5. G. W. BROWN, E. M. MONCK, G. M. CAIRSTAIRS and J. K. WING, Influence of family life on the course of schizophrenic illness, *Brit. J. Prev. Soc. Med.* **16,** 55 (1962).

6. PETER MITTLER, *The Mental Health Services*, Fabian Society publication, 1966.

7. KATHLEEN JONES, British Society Association Conference, 1965.

8. J. TIZARD, *Community Services for the Mentally Handicapped*, O.U.P., 1964.

9. J. TIZARD, R. KING, N. RAYNES and W. YULE, The care and treatment of subnormal children in residential institutions, paper read at Association for Special Education, London, 1966.

CHAPTER 6

1. *Hansard*, Vol. 739, col. 1442, 24 Jan. 1967.

2. E. ROBB, *Sans Everything*, Nelson, 1967.

3. *Hansard*, Vol. 744, col. 537, 7 April 1967.

4. *Administrative Practice of Hospital Boards in Scotland*, H.M.S.O., 1966, (Farquharson-Lang Report).

CHAPTER 7

1. *Children and their Primary Schools*, H.M.S.O., 1967 (Plowden Report).

2. R. W. KNOWLAND, The British Hospital Journal, Nov. 1967.

CHAPTER 8

1. R. P. McMAHON. *The Hospital*, **61,** No. 6, 1965 (pp. 296–8).

2. *Report of the Committee on Senior Nursing Staff Structure*, H.M.S.O., 1966 (The Salmon Committee Report).

3. R. STEVENS, *Medical Care*, pp. 208–13, 1965.

4. *The Shape of Hospital Management in 1980?* Report of Joint Working Party of King's Fund for London and Institute of Hospital Administrators. King's Fund, 1967.

5. *The Internal Administration of Hospitals*, H.M.S.O., 1954 (The Bradbeer Committee Report).

CHAPTER 9

1. J. W. SMITH and E. M. MOTTRAM, *British Medical Journal* **4,** 672 (1967).

2. PETER DRAPER, *Lancet* **2,** 1406 (1967).

Further Reading

1. JULIA PARKER, *Local Health and Welfare Services*, Allen & Unwin, 1965.
ANN CARTWRIGHT, *Patients and Their Doctors*, Routledge and Kegan Paul, 1967.

CHAPTER 10

1. Annual Report of the Ministry of Health, 1966.
2. T. McKeown and I. Leck, Institutional care of the mentally sub-normal, *British Medical Journal* **2,** 573 (1967).
3. P. Sainsbury and J. Grad, Evaluating the community psychiatric services in Chichester, *Millbank Mem. Fund Quarterly*—XLIV No. 1, Part 2.
4. N. Kessel, The evaluation of the Plymouth Nuffield Clinic. *Ibid.*
5. J. W. Brown, M. Bone, B. Dalison and J. K. Wing, *Schizophrenia and Social Care*, O.U.P., 1966.
6. J. W. Brown, E. M. Monck, G. M. Cairstairs and J. W. Wing, Influence of family life on the course of schizophrenic illness, *Brit. J. Prev. Soc. Med.* **16,** 55 (1962).
7. E. M. Monk, Employment experiences of 127 discharged schizophrenic men in London, *Brit. J. Prev. Soc. Med.* **17,** 101 (1963).
8. S. Smith, G. M. Gibb, A. A. Martin, Metamorphosis of a mental hospital, *Lancet* **2,** 592 (1961).
9. A. Kushlick, A method of evaluating the effectiveness of a community health service, *Social and Economic Administration,* **1,** (4) University of Exeter, 1967.
10. G. F. Rehin, H. Houghton and E. M. Martin, Mental health social work in hospitals and local authorities, in *Problems and Progress in Medical Care*, O.U.P., 1964.
11. M. Jeffries, *An Anatomy of Social Welfare Services*, Joseph, 1965.
12. F. M. Martin and G. F. Rehin, *Mental Health Community Services*. In press. O.U.P.
13. R. M. Titmuss, Community care—fact or fiction? in H. G. Freeman and J. Farndale, *Trends in the Mental Health Services*, Pergamon Press, 1961.

CHAPTER 11

1. *Health and Welfare. The development of community care.* Cmd. 1973, 1963.
2. R. Titmuss. Social Work and Social Service. A Challenge for Local Government. *Royal Soc. Health Journal,* **86,** 1966.
3. *Home Office Written Evidence to Royal Commission on Local Government*, H.M.S.O., 1967.
4. Institute of Municipal Treasurers and Accountants. *Memorandum to Committee on Local Authority and Allied Personal Services*, May 1966.

CHAPTER 12

1. *Local Government in Wales*, Cmd. 3340, H.M.S.O., 1967.
2. Sir Robert Aitken, *A Medical View—Is there an Alternative?* British Medical Association, Tavistock Sq.
3. *British Medical Journal Supplement*, 27th January 1968.